CREATIVE ENGINEERING DESIGN

Winner, 1960,
Iowa State University Press Annual Award
for the Most Significant New Book
by an Iowa State Faculty Member

"Don't just sit there — invent something??"

CREATIVE ENGINEERING DESIGN

HAROLD R. BUHL
Department of Mechanical Engineering
Iowa State University

The Iowa State University Press, *Ames,* Iowa

ACKNOWLEDGMENTS

The author wishes to thank the following publications and persons for permission to reproduce cartoons: *Machine Design; Look* and cartoonist Dave Gerard; cartoonist John Bluto and the *Saturday Evening Post; Design News;* and Woods, Gordon & Co., Management Consultants, Toronto, Canada.

Library of Congress catalogue card number 60-12687

To

Naomi, Brian and Susan

Who bring me wonderful, stimulating
and never-ending problems to solve

TABLE OF CONTENTS

1.

Design Creativity - The Challenge

IN THE LATE 1800's, Oliver Wendell Holmes observed that there are one-story intellects, two-story intellects, and three-story intellects. All past collectors of information who have no aim beyond their facts, said Holmes, are one-story men. Two-story men compare, reason, generalize, using the labors of the past collectors as well as their own. *Three-story men idealize, imagine, predict. Their best illumination comes from above—through the skylight.*

In engineering, we are interested in applying man's intellect to satisfy mankind's physical and social needs through the use of the information and theories acquired in science. A designer is one who satisfies mankind's needs through *new* answers to *old* problems. Regardless of formal qualifications, *as a designer,* the first- or second-story man will be no better than mediocre. The designer's *primary responsibility is innovation* through the use of the intellect, and the creative intellect of the third-story man is the essential ingredient for his success. The designer must *deliberately* create new products and processes which will fulfill mankind's needs. He must be creative in *all*

There is no tyrant like custom and no freedom where its edicts are not resisted.
Bovee.

stages of problem solution. In research, in analysis, management, or operation, he must be willing to get off the beaten path or he will arrive at the same solutions as those who have tried before.

In our profession we expend a great deal of effort in modifying modification rather than in attacking the problems at their core. Only a relatively few individuals have thus far been able to overcome the personal and environmental difficulties of problem solving and to rise to become third-story intellects. That mankind's needs have not been satisfied and that there is a need for creative engineers is even superficially evident. Industries are continually being supplanted, not by modifications but by innovations. Locomotives were not displaced by modified locomotives but by a new approach to transportation needs—the car.

See *Creative Engineering* (monograph), by ASME.

A slow sort of country! said the Queen. *Now, here, you see, it takes all the running* you *can do, to keep in the same place. If you want to get somewhere else, you must run at least twice as fast as that!*— Through the Looking-Glass, Lewis Carroll.

Even though we've always had a shortage of creative people and creative ideas, this deficiency is particularly serious today. The last twenty years of science have produced theories and facts at a phenomenal rate, but we are having difficulty assimilating them into our way of life. We shall require more creative individuals to keep us from misusing or wasting the opportunities given to our generation. And even then we shall have to be like Alice who had to run very fast to keep in the same place, and twice as fast to progress.

Until the present day we have sought to expose the student to every conceivable situation he might encounter after he leaves the university. The present growth of technical knowledge has placed this goal beyond the reach of a four-year college education. The student may now be assured that ten or twenty years after graduation many of the problem solutions and "facts" presented to him will have changed. So today's schools must educate the student for change. Students must not only learn the fundamental ideas upon which the various subjects are based but they must learn how to solve a problem in a creative way if possible. However, schools can no longer train *comprehensively* in even a narrow, specialized field. Students cannot possibly be exposed to every situation which they will ever encounter professionally.

In the sciences, there is an ample supply of technicians, but the number who can creatively formulate fruitful hypotheses and theories is small indeed. Carl Rogers.

The purpose of this book is to assist in developing a capacity to design. Each individual needs explicit training in methods of engineering problem solution and in how to apply a wealth of factual information to solve real problems. These training tools are not new but it is the purpose of this book to bring them together in one place. A second purpose, tightly linked with the first, is to become creative in solving these problems. The solution of "scientific" problems is not straightforward and precise but requires the use of the greatest ingenuity.

Each engineer should realize that it is possible to *develop* creative problem solving ability. First, he should acquire all the necessary tools of the profession and gain confidence and proficiency in their application. Then he can combine these tools and procedures with imagination and reason. Without reason he would have mere fantasy and without imagination he would never begin. Usher remarked that "Without imagination an idea is cold and conservative, without call for great achievement."

The engineering profession has a unique opportunity to use its techniques for the deliberate creating of improvements. It also has an equal number of chances to become caught in the mire of perfunctoriness. We in engineering have a tendency to follow paths that have been followed many times before and although we see new and important goals to be reached we often do not build new paths to these because we do not know how to build new paths. In the past we have thought that only those with some inherited ability could create or that creation was spontaneous. Now we know that creativeness can be deliberate and that any engineer can create if he will learn, practice, and apply.

GENERAL PROBLEM SOLVING

LOGICALLY, to develop a systematic procedure for solving engineering problems we should survey problem solving in a general way. With this broad understanding we may proceed to study its application to the field of engineering. Then we will be ready to study a summary of the factors which hinder or aid in the creative solution of these problems.

To understand how a problem is solved, it is desirable to select a problem area common to all of us but free from any emotional connotations which might block our objectivity. Few problems meet both requirements!

Boys and problems seem almost synonymous and few problems are more common than a boy trying to avoid an unpleasant task. Mark Twain collectively combined all our youths into the life of Tom Sawyer and placed him in the epitome of all problems, the unpainted fence. He also placed into this one classic character a method typical of a general procedure to follow in attacking problems, as well as a creative and unconventional attitude toward what constitutes a solution.

Better read the story again (in the Appendix) before going on.

This story, "*The Innocents Beguiled,*" may be found in the back of this book p. 186. It is desirable that you try to analyze the phases or stages involved and observe any factors which tended to produce such a successful and clever solution to a common problem. How would you have solved it?

Let's break the story into its essential phases. There was a problem, without a doubt. The contrast between the lure of a bright and fresh summer morning and "Thirty yards of board fence nine feet high," and a "bucket of whitewash and a long-handled brush" afforded the problem area. However, the problem was not given to Tom as "solve the following" or "determine how to paint a fence."

His first response was to try a quick solution using the many successful solutions to past problems, and perhaps the unsuccessful ones too. He tried to "con" Jim into a trade of duties and he tried brute determination. Both failed, for in this problem there appeared factors not present in previous ones. At first his mind was not able to bridge the gap between the problem area and all combinations of known facts and ideas.

Tom then took stock of the situation, viewed his inventory of possessions, analyzed the data to the extent of determining its insufficiency to solve the problem by the direct approach of bribery or hiring. With the analysis superficially complete, the solution did not present itself until a certain despondency and darkness appeared in his soul. And then "an inspiration burst upon him, nothing less than a great magnificent inspiration."

Tom was then sure of the method to be employed and it was only necessary to present his solution creatively to his unsuspecting fellow creatures. There followed a serenity born of the knowledge that the solution was inherently workable. With a combination of Job's patience and of Solomon's wisdom he put on quite a performance. With an unconventional combination of all the relevant facts, he duped Ben, Tom,

Use margins for notes. This book is meant to be lived in!

Billy Fisher, and Johnny Miller and took their worldly possessions to boot.

The entire problem solving process so unconsciously employed by Tom may be summarized under various headings to permit generalization. There was first a *recognition* phase in which he viewed the data of the beckoning world and the unpainted fence and discovered they were incompatible. Next came the *definition* of the problem. A less creative person might have said "How can I paint the fence with the least expenditure of effort" or "in the least time." His first definition was along this line. However, by redefining it as "How can the fence be painted," the search for solutions was broadened. There was probably a time when the problem was defined as "how can I eliminate the need for painting the fence" but the determination and insistence of Aunt Polly clearly indicated that this was not within the realm of feasibility.

The search phase was initiated by a period of *preparation.* He took stock of all data and of all past and possible solutions. He *analyzed* these to determine their inherent and basic properties. He manipulated or *synthesized* this analyzed information, comparing, contrasting, positioning it with regard to the tremendous problem at hand. He rejected those combinations without merit, being cautious not to discard those with a remote and not so obvious spark of genius. The solution appeared as an inspiration or illumination following a brief period of inactivity on the problem, a period of incubation.

It was then necessary to conduct an *evaluation* of its merits, to make checks on the assumptions and the data, and to develop the idea in greater detail. It was finally necessary to effect a *presentation* of the solution in a manner consistent with all the facts yet creative enough to overcome, on the part of the recipients, any natural caution and resistance to change.

Method is like packing things in a box; a good packer will get in half as much again as a bad one. Cecil.

Here, then, are the elements of problem solving. It would be erroneous to say that these steps were followed in precisely a 1, 2, 3, manner. It was surely impossible to determine precisely the nature of the problem until some earlier solutions had failed. It was necessary to repeat and to retrace the steps until finally all the factors were consistent with the possible solution.

This system is not a panacea. It does free our minds of the routine planning and reserves for it the truly creative tasks. System performs a function similar to habit in driving a car. To require an individual to drive, consciously performing every action, would prohibit the execution of the task. Habit does not obviate the need of judgment, of decision making, of searching for possible solutions as each problem arises in the operation of the car.

A system in itself would not produce anything more than routine answers to problems. It is necessary to understand all the factors which tend to prohibit or retard the work at each phase, and to understand what things tend to increase the possibility of an unusual answer. It is essential that all the creative work be built upon a firm foundation of a method of solving problems. When this is mastered, it will only be necessary to increase the solver's proficiency in each phase in order to improve his ingenuity.

It must be mentioned that the solution used by Tom was not the only possible solution nor was it necessarily the most appropriate or most creative. It was *a* creative solution. All human needs can be met with many solutions, the appropriateness of which will vary with each situation and problem. This multiplicity of answers is both a valuable tool in our behalf and also a tremendous mental block.

Solving Design Problems

IN BRIEF, to solve a problem, we associate past experiences with the problem situation and try to arrive at a workable combination. The mind, being an emergency organ, attempts to solve the problem from habit, by fitting previously successful solutions to current problems of a similar nature. Should these past solutions prove unworkable the mind may attempt to solve the problem by using more remote associations some of which may be accepted even though they introduce additional problems. Solving problems by habit may also cause us to continue trying solutions which we know are unsuccessful. So acts the fly trying to get out of a partially open window—he tries to fly through the glass even though freedom is available through the open portion only inches away.

Habit is either the best of servants, or the worst of masters. Emmons.

We should *not* conclude that habit can't be used because it often leads to undesirable solutions. Habit performs a very useful task in saving our minds for the difficult tasks. Should we consciously try to solve each and every problem which arises as we drive from here to there we should soon lose our sanity. Such was the case of the young man sorting potatoes who had to quit because there were too many decisions to make. The disadvantage of using habit as a sole means of problem solution is that we may pass up more desirable solutions which might be gained by new associations.

On Problem Solving, Karl Duncker; also *Productive Thinking,* Max Wertheimer. (See Bibliography.)

When habit fails to solve the problem we must make a more systematic attempt. It must be realized that the only raw material available for solving problems is past knowledge. This does not mean that it must come from our own experiences. It may come from others and be communicated to us. These bits of information must then be combined in an effective way. Often, our habits prevent us from making useful combinations and cause us to be mechanized in our procedures and rigid in the way we see things. Ways of overcoming such mental blocks will be discussed later.

Invention is little more than a new combination of those images which have been previously gathered and deposited in the memory. Nothing can be made of nothing; he who has laid up no materials can produce no combinations. Sir Joshua Reynolds.

How we organize our problem solving depends upon our own personality, our own experiences, and our own values (what we consider important in life). One person may emphasize the discovery of truth. Another, with a high need for social acceptance, may emphasize the acceptance of the problem solution and how it will be used. Another person, interested in personal power, will emphasize status and prestige. Each, therefore, will take a somewhat different approach to the problem. Lifelong values together with daily fluctuations in feelings and attitudes also will influence people in problem solving situations.

See *The Nature of Creative Thinking.*

Another kind of person sees problems as a stimulus to action and tends to avoid any intense analysis, while a highly theoretical person finds enjoyment in abstract conceptions and tends to avoid empirical relationships. There are those who like to see relationships between problems and between ideas. Others find motivation in the gathering of facts and observations. These individual styles must be accounted for in problem solving. The following phases of the procedure must be adapted to the person and to the environment in which that person solves problems.

Excellent articles are in "Innovation in Science" issue of *Scientific American,* Sept., 1958.

The procedures of problem solving have been stated with reasonable agreement by various men. Much of the early writing concerned itself with the listing of experiences in solving specific problems. Through the years records have been kept of the thought processes of various men, including many scientists, musicians—such as Mozart, artists, and others. In 1926 Graham Wallas and in 1933 John Dewey analyzed the various processes. Many present-day educators agree with these basic ideas. However, it should be emphasized that the steps are neither sacred nor chronological. These steps indicate phases to be covered in an approximate order. Practice may require starting at some intermediate point, and repeating many steps. Many of the steps will occur unconsciously, particularly in simple problems.

These steps may be summarized as follows:

Recognition of the problem and decision to do something about it.

Definition of the problem specifically, in familiar terms and symbols; dissection of the problem into subproblems and goals, placement of the necessary limitations and restrictions.

Preparation by compilation of all past experience in the form of data, ideas, opinions, assumptions, and the like.

Analysis of all the preparatory material in view of the defined problems, interrelation, comparison, evaluation of all information which may have bearing upon a solution.

Synthesis of a solution from analyzed information. Assemblage of the various items analyzed to produce possible solutions.

Evaluation of possible solutions, and selection. Verification and checking of various facets of the solution and coordination of all sub-problem solutions into an integrated whole. A decision.

Presentation of necessary information to others in order to execute the solution. Activation of the solution to satisfy the need recognized.

These phases of problem solving and design may be represented in graphical form. In the recognition stage the designer finds a problem situation or "mess." In this phase the problem is without form, rather vague as follows:

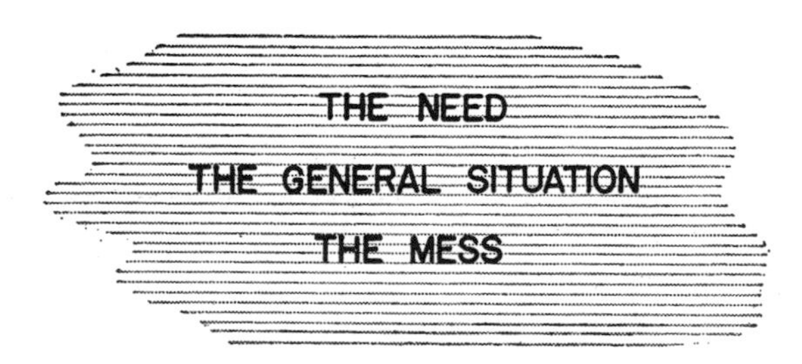

The designer must then bring form or orderliness out of this situation by determining the specific problem to be solved (basic function, reliability, producibility, operation, etc.) and the requirements which any solution must meet.

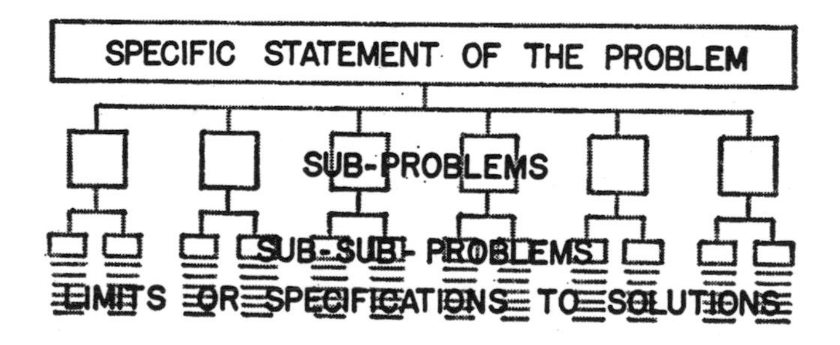

Opposed to the problem itself is the vast amount of material out of which a solution may be formed. The ideas, observations, measurements, past solutions, analytical procedures of all history are available as a mass of preparatory material.

This mass is again formless much as the problem area was at first. To bring understanding and form out of this tremendous amount of data, we must analyze it to find out those few basic ideas which have some potential bearing on the problem.

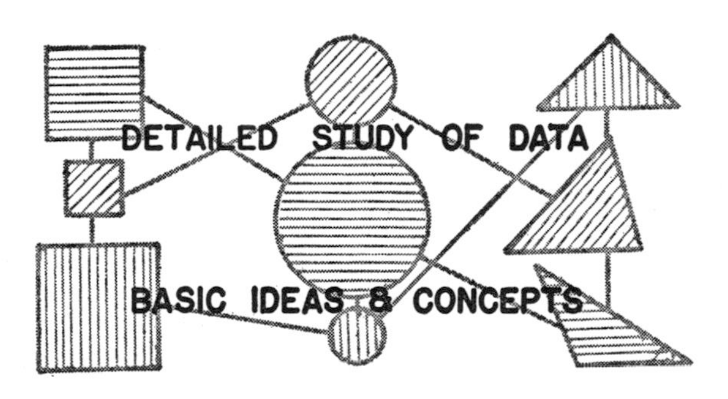

At this stage two areas exist: (1) the problem itself—broken down and studied, and (2) the material out of which a solution must come. The data have been studied or analyzed to determine inner relationships. These two areas are then brought together or the gap bridged by synthesis to produce solutions.

These solutions are combinations and arrangements of the analyzed data and the specific problems.

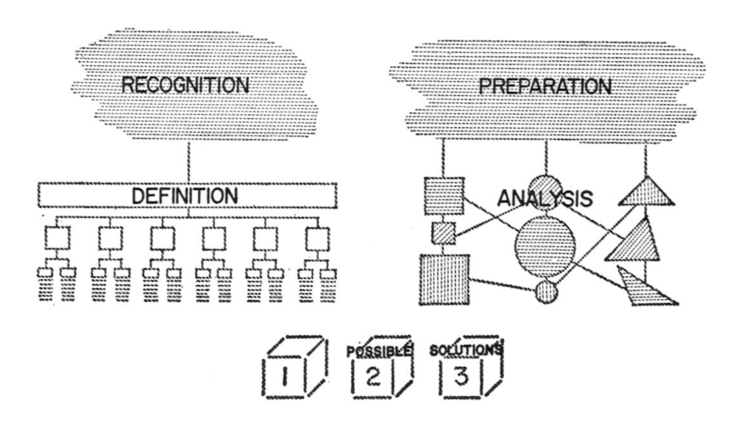

The possible solutions must be compared and judged. The designer must usually select one solution to recommend weighing the relative merits of each potential solution.

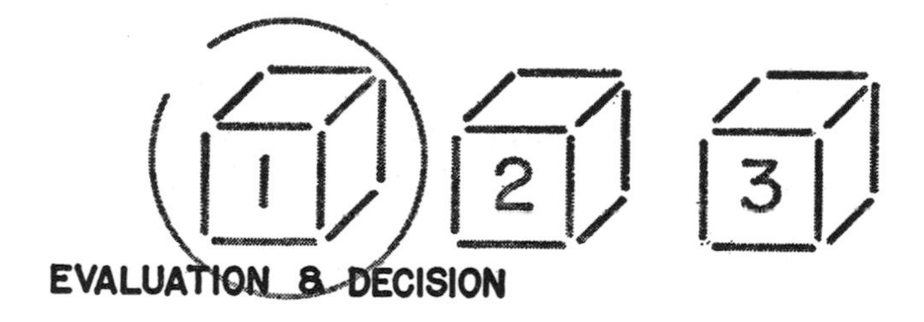

The selected solution must then be put into effect, that is, adopted.

The following procedure furnishes a structure under which the problem area and past experiences may be combined effectively to produce a solution.

The procedure incorporates these various phases which will be studied in detail in following chapters:

1. *Establish* a problem area — **recognize**
2. *Determine* exactly the nature of the problem — **define**
3. *Collect* pertinent information — **prepare**
4. *Break down and study* this information — **analyze**
5. *Assemble* the analyzed information into various configurations — **synthesize**
6. *Study* the merits of each possible solution and select — **evaluate**
7. *Sell* the chosen solution — **present**

No known formula exists to insure creative thought, but an individual plan of action can be developed to cover the necessary phases of thought. All that can be expected is that creative thinking is more likely to result from a carefully engineered approach.

The following problem solutions are given to show the application of this procedure to the solution of actual problems.

Sample Problem Solutions

PROBLEM 1. The following is a mathematical game:

1. select any 4-digit number, say 1734
2. add the digits 15
3. subtract this sum from the original number 1719
4. cross out one of the digits of this result, say 7 1719

5. add the remaining digits 11
6. present this sum (11) to the individual presenting the problem whereupon he tells you that you crossed out the number 7.

Repeat the procedure:

1. select say 9438
2. add the digits 24
3. subtract the sum from the original number 9414
4. cross out one of the digits, say 4 9414
5. add the remaining digits 14
6. present this sum to the individual presenting the problem whereupon he tells you that you crossed out the number 4.

If now the problem solving procedures are applied to this situation and if this procedure assists us in attaining a solution, it may be concluded that the procedure possesses some merit.

Recognition. There must be some logical explanation as to why this unusual procedure works. Since this explanation is not readily apparent, the problem area consists of an unexplained phenomenon.

Definition. Two problem parts may be defined: 1. What procedures were used in determining the number crossed out? 2. Why does this procedure work? What mathematical or logical reasons exist that permit the puzzle to operate?

Solution for Part 1. Since we are concerned mainly with part 2 of the problem area, the solution of part 1 may be discovered either by determining the common factors in numerous applications of the problem or by being illuminated by the individual who presents the problem. The difference between the sum of the remaining digits at step (4) and a multiple of 9 is the digit crossed out.

Preparation. Solution for Part 2. The following pieces of information may be determined:

1. Any number may be crossed out anywhere in the sequence.

2. Any original number apparently works (the 4-digit limitation may or may not be significant).
3. General numbers and digits may be converted to symbols and manipulated by algebraic rules.
4. It may be possible to assume the procedure works and then test to see if this results in requiring the limitations which we have imposed upon the problem.

Analysis. Conversion to familiar mathematical symbols.

1. A general 4-digit number may be represented by the symbol $ABCD$ where A, B, C, and D represent whole numbers 1, 2, 3, 4, 5, 6, 7, 8, 9 or 0.
2. The sum of these digits may be represented by $A+B+C+D$.
3. Step 3 may be represented as $ABCD-(A+B+C+D)=EFGH$ where E, F, G, and H are whole numbers from 1 thru 0 and may be the same as A, B, C, and D.
4. One digit is then crossed out $EFGH$; the cross-out being arbitrary.
5. The sum of the remaining digits is $E+G+H$.
6. The answer (according to problem 1) is $9N-(E+G+H)=F$ where N is a whole number.

Synthesis:

a. The rules of algebra may permit manipulation into a situation in which the answer is known. Two areas of the above give promise of offering clues. It appears to the individual that there must exist some relationship between a number and the sum of its digits. Also, step 6 should offer possibilities if written in a more familiar manner. Try substitution.

b. By investigating what is meant by a number $ABCD$, we may conclude that this also means $(A\times10^3+B\times10^2+C\times10+D)-(A+B+C+C)$ form of a sum of digits. Likewise with $EFGH$. Therefore step 3 may be rewritten as
$(A\times10^3+B\times10^2+C\times10+D)-(A+B+C+C)$
$=E\times10^3+F\times10^2+G\times10+H$.

c. Step 6 may be rearranged to be
$9N=E+F+G+H$.

d. What connection is there between b and c if A, B, C, D, E, F, G, H and N are integers? Let's assume the equations are valid and determine if the symbols must be always integers.

e. Write
$(A\times10^3+B\times10^2+C\times10+D)-(A+B+C+D)$
$=(E\times10^3+F\times10^2+G\times10+H)$.
Does $9N=E+F+G+H$?

f. Try simplification into one equation by factoring
$(E\times10^3+F\times10^2+G\times10+H)$
$=(E+F+G+H)+(999E+99F+9G)$.

g. Then by substitution does:
$(E\times10^3+F\times10^2+G\times10+H)$
$=9N+(999E+99F+9G)$?

h. Try simplification of left side of (e); does
$999A+99B+9C=9N+(999E+99F+9G)$?

i. Note the pattern; try simplification; does
$111(A-E)+11(B-F)+(C-G)=N$?
Does the left side always equal a whole number? Yes, since A, B, C, E, F, G are always integers.

Evaluation:

1. The above system will work for 4-digit numbers and larger.
2. The above proof indicates that the system works not because of chance but because the operations are consistent with the rules of algebra.

Here a problem of a mathematical nature has been solved. (Many other ways could have been used.) An attempt was made to delineate the phases or steps involved. No attempt was made to explain why the various things were tried or how it happened that the solver thought of these ideas. This will be reserved for subsequent development when these steps are discussed in greater detail and when a discussion is presented as to why individuals are not more creative. Let it suffice to say here that the ideas came about by mental manipulation, by trial and error, intuition and the like, and that this process, constituting the bulk of what we call creativity, can be *consciously* and *deliberately* developed and achieved.

PROBLEM 2. The following problem of a mathematical nature should serve to further illuminate the phases involved in the solution of problems.

"A 6-digit number in which the first three digits are repeated to make the second half of the number is always divisible by 13. For example, numbers of the form 271,271 or 582,582, etc. are all divisible by 13."

Recognition. There appears to be an orderly procedure here and we can expect therefore a scientific or mathematical explanation for this unusual situation. Merely to divide any arbitrary number by 13 does not prove that *all* such numbers would work equally well.

Definition. The problem is to discover, if possible, the mathematical reason why such a number is divisible by 13 and to show thereby that *all* such numbers are divisible by 13.

Preparation. The number has a certain sequence:

1. It is always a 6-digit number.
2. 13 is a prime number.
3. The magnitude of the digits is unimportant so long as the sequence is adhered to.

Analysis. This number may be represented by the symbols *abc,abc* where *a, b* and *c* are digits from 1 through 0.

Synthesis. The sequence constitutes an unusual configuration of numbers. Fundamentally, how is this sequence obtained?

Analysis. *Abc,abc* is the product of *abc* and some number whose digits are such that when multiplication is performed, the numbers not only repeat themselves, but remain unchanged in either the 1st or 2nd group. $1001 \times abc$ meets these requirements.

Synthesis. Since 1001 is a common factor of all these numbers, perhaps there are common factors in the common factor.

Analysis. 1001 is composed of the product of the following prime numbers $13 \times 11 \times 7$.

Presentation. It is therefore concluded that 13 and 11 and 7 are common factors of all 6-digit numbers of the form *abc,abc*. The number *abc,abc* is therefore always divisible by 13. It is also always divisible by 7 and 11.

The problem as presented here is rather brief. This does not indicate that it is simple nor that the time for solution was brief. To know where to look for synthesis and how to analyze the problem are tasks which not only consume time but involve insight, intuition and above all trial-and-error. The unprofitable dead-end trials have not been included here. Often we are not even conscious of the multitude of the acts of analysis and synthesis which our mind makes. Usually only the promising ones appear to our consciousness.

PROBLEM 3. The following problem is intended to show that we have within each of us the potential for solving problems if we will but be confident that by work, self examination, and questioning, we can solve a problem. Most of us have in the past been persuaded to memorize solutions to the following problem but the fundamental facts and concepts required are relatively few. We should be able to reproduce answers such as this without resort to memorization.

Recognition. We learn from our study of various geometric shapes that the sum of the angles of a rectangle is 360° and that of a triangle is 180°. We often wonder perhaps why this must be so or what would be the sum of the angles on a 5-sided figure.

Definition. What is the sum of all the angles in an N-sided polygon?

Preparation:

1. A polygon of N sides involves N straight lines and N angles. All these lines are connected. It is a closed figure which means that when traversing the perimeter of the figure we may return to the

starting point without retracing the lines or without lifting the pencil.

2. It appears that the limit of N sides would be something like a circle.

Analysis. A straight line is known to represent 180°.

Synthesis. A polygon of N sides contains N straight lines the product of N and 180° may be involved in the solution.

Analysis. For a triangle $N=3$; therefore $3 \times 180° = 540°$; it is known a triangle contains 180° so the excess is 360°. For a square, $N=4$; therefore $4 \times 180° = 720°$; it is known that a square contains 360°. The excess is 360°, the same as for a triangle. Perhaps this is significant.

Analysis. As stated in the preparation, the polygon is composed of straight lines connected to form a closed figure permitting return to the starting point. When N is increased, the number of straight lines increases. This may be accomplished by bending an existing line. To do this two of the angles increase but the straight line changes from 180° to something less. In going from a triangle to a square it does not appear that the sum of the angles should increase by 100 per cent.

Synthesis. It appears that if the figure is composed of a series of straight lines returning to the starting point, and all straight lines are an identical 180°, then the figure could perhaps be formed by manipulating only *one* line into various positions to form the polygon. How would this work on a triangle?

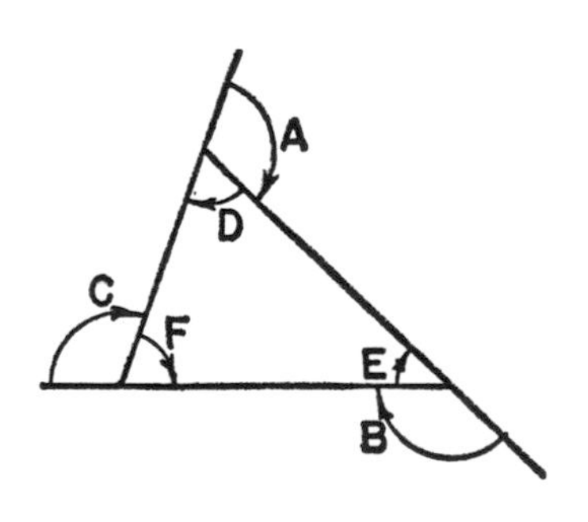

Analysis. To draw a triangle, take a straight line, then rotate it through some arbitrary angle (for the general case). Do this three times returning to the starting line. The fact that it is a closed figure means I've rotated the one line 360°. (Same magnitude as error in original assumption—could there be some significance?) This 360° then represents the sum of A, B and C in the following figure. The straight lines are then represented by the sums of A and D, B and E, C and F. The sum of D, E and F constitutes the solution which we are seeking, the sum of the angles of a polygon. The triangle then is made with three angles D, E, and F made by three straight lines which also contain the excess angles A, B and C. The sum of these angles is always 360°. This may be formulated as:

Sum of the angles of a polygon
$= N$ straight lines $-360°$
$= N \times 180° - 360° = N \times 180° - 2 \times 180° = (N-2)$ 180°

Evaluation. For a triangle $N=3$. Then $(N-2)\,180° = 1 \times 180° = 180°$. OK

For square $N=4$. Then $(N-2)\ 180° = 2 \times 180° = 360°$. OK

For pentagon $N=5$. Sum$=3 \times 180° = 540°$. If the pentagon is divided into five isosceles triangles, each center angle is $360°/5 = 72°$. This leaves $180-72 = 108°$ as the sum of the other two angles of each triangle. With five triangles, the sum of all such angles is 540°. OK

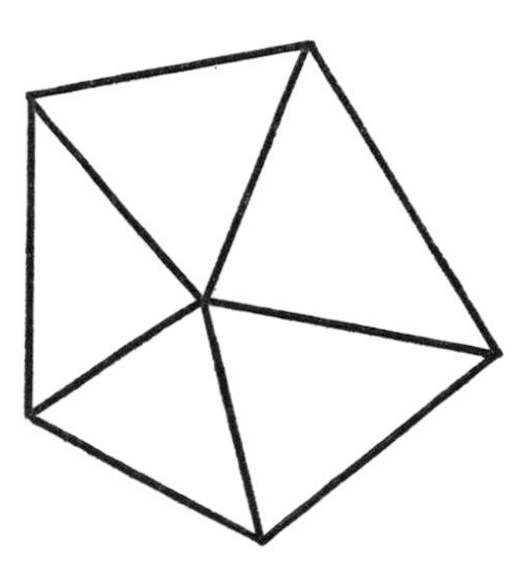

The steps appear logical and the results of a finite and small number of polygons appears consistent with the formula.

Presentation. The sum of all the angles of a polygon is $(N-2) \times 180°$ where N is the number of sides of the polygon. This is the sum whether or not the polygon is regular and symmetrical.

PROBLEM 4. How would you solve the problem of the butter conditioner?

We have all experienced the difficulty of spreading hard butter on a piece of fresh bread, and likewise we have experienced the unsatisfactory taste of warm, greasy butter. These two extreme conditions prompted the Household Refrigerator Department to install in some of their deluxe models a "butter conditioner." This device maintains the butter at spreading temperature which by test is found to be $60 \pm 5°$ F.

The present design (Fig. 1, next page) consists of the compartment capable of holding one pound of butter in a conventional butter dish. This compartment is deep drawn of 0.040″ aluminum and is installed in the door of the refrigerator. A thermostatically controlled heater is installed in the bottom of the compartment. The heater is a simple, enclosed, resistance-type heater.

FIG. 1

HEATER, THERMOSTAT AND CONTROL KNOB

This butter conditioner has a compartment ambient characteristic similar to that shown in Fig. 2 when the thermostat is set to hold 60° F. in the compartment.

FIG. 2

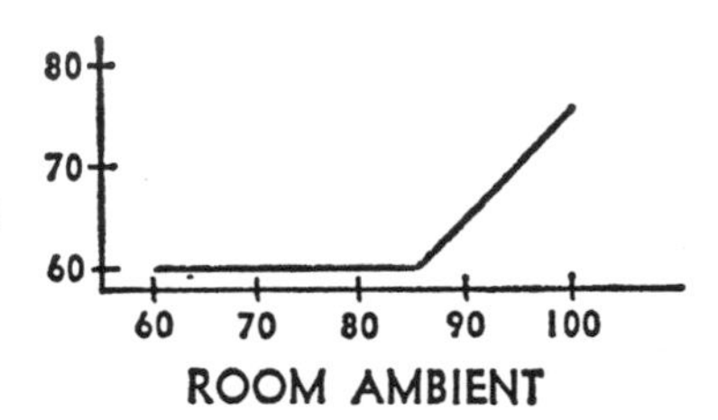

BUTTER CONDITIONER TEMPERATURE

When the room ambient exceeds a certain amount, the heater no longer operates and the temperature in the butter conditioner starts to increase because of heat leakage through the insulation.

We would like to know the lowest wattage heater that is required to maintain the butter conditioner temperature for room ambients as low as 60° F.

The initial cost of the heater and thermostat and the associated wiring is high. Assuming that the ambient always surpasses good spreading temperature and the cabinet air temperature is always less, it appears that some method of controlling the heat leakage could be used to maintain a butter conditioner temperature that is adequate.

Some of the systems proposed to do this give a characteristic as shown in Fig. 3.

This is not completely satisfactory, for the ideal would be a horizontal line. The question at hand is: How can the heat leakage be controlled so that the slope of the butter conditioner temperature-ambient temperature characteristic is decreased?

BUTTER CONDITIONER TEMPERATURE

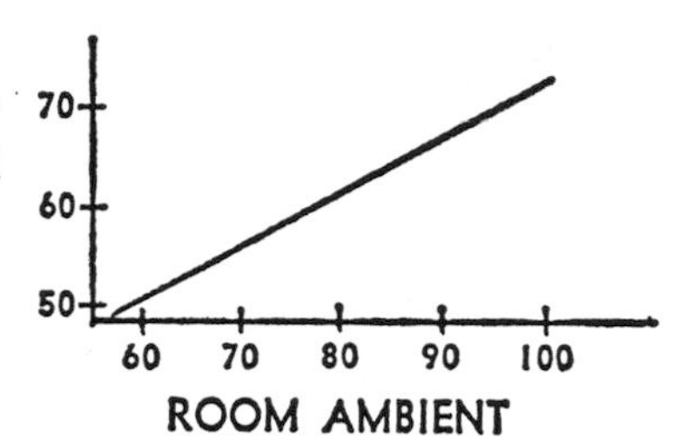

FIG. 4

33°F TO 40°F

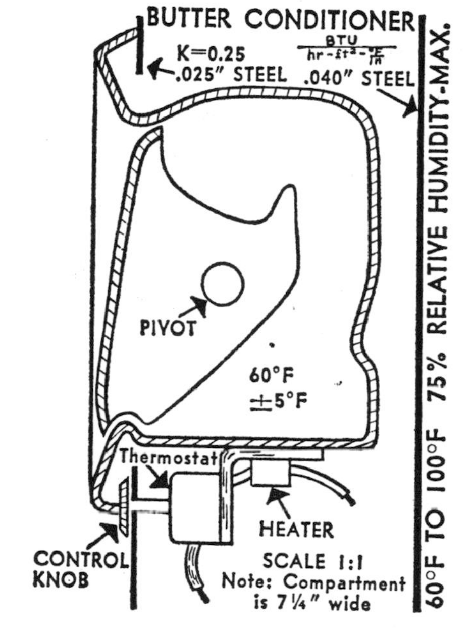

(*General Electric Co.*)

There may be other ways of keeping butter at the right temperature. What suggestions can you make along this line?

Using the Problem Approach to Solve Butter Conditioner Problem

Recognition. The problem has been recognized before being presented to the class.

Definition. The problem definition can be considered in four basic steps:

Initial word statement. An initial statement of the problem is given in the written problem statement. Ordinarily this serves to insure that you and the boss have agreed on what you are trying to determine from your study.

Initial specifications. Several important initial specifications are included in the written problem statement. Consider that there may be others, such as cost and space limitations.

Analysis. Study the butter conditioner intensively, using any analytical or experimental techniques you feel necessary. For instance, you may study the heat flow around the butter-conditioner unit by making a "small squares flux plot" or by making a quick calculation of the heat lost. On the other hand, you may desire to build a model and perform a calorimeter test. With any method, from this phase you determine the power required and the heater wattage rating.

Modify initial specifications. From your investigation you may have learned certain information that permits you to make modifications of your initial specifications. For example, you may learn that the present size or spacing of the butter conditioner is inadequate. You will later judge your results on the basis of these final specifications.

Synthesis. Now you consider other possible designs of the device: How about a moving door controlled by a thermostatic spring? Perhaps a set of louvers controlled by a thermostat? Could you let warm air in from the outside by varying the insulation properties in some way as a function of heat required? List as many ideas as possible so that you have a maximum chance of thinking up a really good one.

Evaluation of the Methods. Develop each idea a little further so that you can begin to judge its worth. Ask yourself: What are the good points of each?

How is it better than the others? Also consider the disadvantages of each.

Selection of Method. Choose the design of butter conditioner that seems most promising for further development. You must choose a method that will fit the final specifications set down earlier.

Analysis. You now further develop your chosen design. Determine such things as shape, size, weight, and cost. Draw a detailed sketch. Make certain that it can be manufactured with available facilities. Determine the changes that will be necessary in the current manufacturing technique.

Evaluation. Critically appraise your preliminary design: Does it meet your specifications? Will it maintain the required butter temperature? Is it too expensive to produce and market? Is your design —the best solution you have found—really better than the present design? Is the idea really worth more effort? If so, continue to the next step.

Detailed Solution or Design. Complete your design, preparing it for manufacture. Remove the last few bugs that you discovered during your recent interpretation of the results of your design.

(In this solution we have applied the problem approach in a step-by-step fashion. In some problems these steps might be arranged in a different manner. For example, after performing your interpretation of results, you may find that you must again modify your specifications because of new information learned. If so, you may have to revert to the third step, search for methods, and follow through the succeeding solution steps again.)

Remember—make notes. Develop your own problem-solving procedures by using this book as a starter.

HERE'S THE SOLUTION CHOSEN FOR PRODUCTION

THE REFRIGERATOR engineers responsible for the design made the following design changes:

1. The butter conditioner case could be made entirely of plastics.
2. For some refrigerator models the design specifications were changed to provide slightly broader limits of allowable temperature variation. This

permitted a design with no heater. A design was evolved that, by proper control of cabinet heat leakage, allowed heat to be supplied to the butter conditioner from the external ambient air.

3. In some models where more definite temperature control was necessary, the heater was retained, with a new design resistance heater being used.

2.

Recognition

THE INITIAL PHASE in the solution of engineering problems is the recognition that a "mess" exists. Since an engineer is a person who applies scientific knowledge to satisfy mankind's needs, his first task is to determine what and where a need exists. In the design process the engineer attempts to satisfy this need in a manner consistent with the time and facilities available and with the present status of his art.

I cannot imagine why I did not see the elementary facts more clearly than I did. I came to Mr. Edison a trained man, with a year's experience in Helmholtz's laboratory, a working knowledge of calculus, and a mathematical turn of mind. Francis Upton.

The necessity for a creative approach in this phase should be evident. The engineer, in order to function to the limit of his potential, must have a sensitivity for the problems which exist. He must possess constructive discontent regarding his environment, nonconformity regarding possible solutions, and an inquisitive "why" attitude regarding the causes of his observations. If he is to do a better job than his predecessors, he must possess an inner locus of evaluation which motivates him to try to solve the problem regardless of the nature of the difficulties.

Some will never learn anything because they understand everything too soon. Blount.

In his work he is continually hindered by various cultural, emotional and perceptual blocks. The way we see things and the way we think problems *should* be solved, continually prevents us from applying old lessons to new situations. Individually and in groups we resist change, we fear the unknown and what it might do to us. We desire the certainty of the present solution in preference to a new and perhaps better one. We often fail to see objects and problems in an entirely different light. The study of the history of science gives us fascinating insight into the limitations imposed upon fields of study by such blocks. For example, the development of a successful explanation for motion was delayed because people figured that the earth must be the center of rotation of the solar system. They further concluded from their observations that gravity might be explained by saying all objects tended to return to their "home" which was the earth. The development of chemistry was delayed because individuals interpreted chemical reactions as resulting from only four elements: earth, water, air, and fire. It was necessary that these perceptual blocks be overcome before these sciences could progress.

It is a profound mistake to think that everything has been discovered; as well think the horizon the boundary of the world. Lemierre.

We may therefore conclude that an engineer must possess not only scientific knowledge and training and technical know-how but must be sensitive to the problems which exist, must be constructively discontented with the partial solutions and compromises to the problems as they are now solved, and must be cognizant of any blocks which might stand in his way to solutions.

WHAT PROBLEMS EXIST?

The Autobiography of Lincoln Steffens, (1931).

LINCOLN STEFFENS wrote, "The world is yours. Nothing is done, nothing is known. The greatest poem isn't written, the best railroad isn't built yet, the perfect state hasn't been thought of. Everything remains to be done—right, everything." All solutions are the result of compromises with the ability of man, the skills and materials which exist, and the environment in which the solution must operate. Materials, environments, and people change in time and therefore, compromises which are optimum today must change tomorrow. When our national life was largely agrarian, we were satisfied with slow transportation. However, as our nation became more industrial, the requirement for faster travel became more urgent. In frontier days when the problems of mere existence were barely solved, not much attention was paid to our needs of comfort and communication. But as basic needs are satisfied and as more time becomes available, our attention shall be focused more and more upon the problems which exist because of spare time and longevity.

Industry does not prize men who lack values and principles of their own and who seek to please by uncritical acceptance of beliefs and choices. Robert Baxton.

Again, engineering progress lies in the satisfaction of mankind's needs. But what are the needs? To determine them is a problem for the social sciences. A partial list of human needs follows, and it is suggested that the reader may want to add to it: *Food* - production, distribution, preservation, preparation, use; *Water* - production, distribution, use; *Shelter* - individual and group, human, animal, inanimate objects, various elements; *Transportation* - individual, group; *Communication* - aural, symbolic - words, pictures, temporary and permanent; *Exchange of physical objects like money; Recreation; Social needs; Health and sanitation; Air.*

To the thinker, the most trifling external object often suggests ideas, which extend, link after link, from earth to heaven. Bulwer.

Frequently the problem is confined to very narrow limits. Very often in industry a device or solution already exists; it is not desirable to return to the original fundamental problem. Restrictions of economics, of industrial organization, force us to solve the problem within extremely narrow limits. Under these conditions we are interested only in improving a product or machine and this might be accomplished by one or more of the following approaches.

1. Increasing the machine function.
2. Making it do more than it ever did before.
3. Accomplishing its objectives by new approaches.
4. Increasing its advantages insofar as making it longer lived, more reliable, more accurate, safer, more convenient, easier to repair and maintain.
5. Eliminating disadvantages by making the product less expensive, cutting out excess parts, substitution of less costly materials, more efficient manufacturing methods, convenience of assembly, reduction of hand labor, or by redesigning for automatic production and assembly.

Areas involving large expenditures of money may prove fruitful for problem finding. A thorough evaluation of compromises made often results in new designs not incorporating such compromises. We must be cautious, however, to avoid the continual modification of modifications. This seldom results in a creative solution to the problem.

SUB-PROBLEMS

It should be apparent that each of the problems may be broken down into sub-problems and sub-sub-problems. The solutions to these problems must satisfy various requirements. For example, the problem of individual transportation has certain limits of economy and cost, of safety and convenience, of operation, of reliability, of adaptability, and time. The solution involves compromises. In time, such compromises may change, and require new solutions.

Much attention is yet being given to the problem of submarines as possible offensive and defensive weapons. In this general problem area there are four classes of sub-problems which remain unsolved.

1. *Detection.* It is at present impossible to consistently find enemy submarines at any realistic distances. Present-day radar cannot penetrate water, and sonar is almost useless against widely scattered submarines.
2. *Communication.* Our submarines are unable, when submerged, to communicate with aircraft or distant surface ships.
3. *Killing Power.* We do not have available weapons capable of destroying the enemy at adequate

ranges and speed. Current depth charges and torpedoes must be delivered at very short range.

4. *Forces at Sea.* The problem of keeping these forces active and up-to-date is complicated by limitations of funds and manpower. It is necessary to provide adequate protection without causing the economic failure of our nation.

TYPES OF PROBLEMS

IT MIGHT BE well here to study the types of problems which exist. These might be classified as follows:

1. *Those requiring a factual answer.* For example, What time is it? How many BTU are transferred per unit of time from a material to a fluid? What is the stress which exists at a certain point in a shaft? These questions imply certain assumptions and limitations. In general, only one answer exists for each of these questions. However, much creativity is required in the selection and the use of the analytical procedures leading up to such an answer.
2. *Those requiring a judgment such as yes, no, maybe.* Will the machine work? Should the design be accepted? Should the design go into production now? A significant amount of creativity is required in accumulating the necessary information, and analyzing and evaluating it.
3. *How questions.* How can I design an engine which will produce a greater amount of power at a lower cost? How can I increase the amount of heat transferred through a given area in a given period of time? How can I reduce the size of the part and still have it function properly? This type of question requires a high degree of creative ability in order to properly define the problem, adequately prepare for its solution, analyze the accumulated

What we know here is very little, but what we are ignorant of is immense. Laplace.

data, synthesize a solution, successfully evaluate each proposal, and finally, execute the solution.

The "how" problems can be most conveniently solved by attempting to reconstruct them as questions falling in the first or second category. Such reconstructed questions then have factual answers. If the problem is, How can I physically produce it?—the designer may be able to restate the problem as: What physical shapes is it possible to produce on a given machine; How much time is necessary to machine this part on this machine; In what physical shape must the material be in to use this machine; What degree of finish can I obtain on a given machine?

Other "how" questions which might exist in the development of a product are: How can I keep the cost within an acceptable range; How can I make it safe to use; How can I make it reliable in operation; How can we distribute and sell the product; How can I design it so that the operator can operate the device? Each of these questions may then be rephrased to produce factual answers.

It should be noted that in the solution of a problem certain questions are of more significance than others and serve as the key for the solution. Therefore, we must creatively determine which of these problems constitutes the key to the total solution.

FORM OF PROBLEM AREA

THE FORM in which the problem is often presented to an engineer constitutes one of the most serious difficulties which he must overcome. There is a story about an engineer who received the usual four years of analytical training in an engineering college. He arrived at his first job but was soon forced to admit failure. He confided to a friend that had he been given *problems* to solve he could have handled them

Think wrongly, if you please; but in all cases think for yourself. Lessing.

very well. Unfortunately, all he had been given was a mess. But this is the *usual* form in which we find the problem.

Even if some goals are given to the engineer, they are often not specifically stated. We find problems presented to us as—"the shaft is breaking," "the controls aren't producing the desired effect," "it costs too much to operate this engine." It is then the first task of the engineer to determine the real problems which exist and to determine the extent and confines of the goals. Unless the goalsetter has been acting creatively the goals may be undesirable when compared with what could be achieved with the same or less expenditure of time and money.

HOW TO FIND THE PROBLEMS

How MIGHT we obtain these problems? We might easily sit back and wait for the task or some individual to come to us. However, our basic task in engineering is innovation. It is our job to recognize and anticipate problems since any fool can see them when they actually occur. We might obtain them by studying the needs of people both now and in the future. A bridge might be built to handle our present traffic. However, it might be well to also investigate the need for possibly carrying railroad tracks, for supporting power lines, for foot travel, or for carrying water or fuel supplies. In addition we might attempt to anticipate the type and quantity of vehicles which might be in existence say 20 years from the present when the design will still be expected to be performing its function. We might do so by attempting to anticipate or to speculate what life would be like should families become larger, should the work week be shortened, should the average age of people become greater.

A man would do well to carry a pencil in his pocket, and write down the thought of the moment. Those that come unsought for are commonly the most valuable, and should be secured, because they seldom return. Bacon.

We might further determine existing problems by studying the deficiencies of present solutions. Regarding the design of the bridge we might conclude that present bridges are rather heavy, that they require costly maintenance, that they are not readily adapted to changing requirements, that they are subject to functional failure due to vibrations, that they require a significant period of time to erect, that the initial investment is rather large.

1915 Model T Sedan

We did it before — Why can't we do it again?
It fits! In garage and parking space —
The kind of seat that lets you sit
the way nature intended you to;
Easy debugging of the radiator;
Reasonable clearance under car for maintenance;
No windshield distortion;
Step, not crawl inside;
You can see over the hood;
Easy access to the carburetor and spark plugs;
No big bills for dented fenders;
You can get at the spare tire and at the flat one too;
Your throttle foot doesn't get tired (hand throttle);
It'll turn around in an alley or street.

We might also uncover significant problems by mere speculation. The individual might say to himself: "What would happen if I did a certain thing? Perhaps I can substitute concrete for steel or wood. Perhaps I can put the supporting structure below rather than above the roadway. Perhaps I can make the floor of the bridge open rather than solid. Perhaps I can find a solution to this problem by studying the solution to another problem. Perhaps the solution of an electrical problem will give me some ideas for determining the structure of a muffler or the shape of a pressure tank."

With willing hands and open minds, the future will be greater than the most fantastic story you can write. You will always underrate it. Kettering.

It is well to note here that the solutions of the past were based on certain assumptions which were thought necessary due to the materials or procedures which existed at the time. It is also rather valuable to review such solutions to determine what new methods of manufacture, what new materials, or new analytical procedures now exist to solve the problems more adequately. We are now able to use computing machines to arrive at the optimum set of variables in the design of gears, processes, engines, and other systems. We might determine what current trends exist, what is new and whether we can use it, what new solutions have been developed in related or unrelated fields.

Even if it turns out that the ancients discovered everything, the application, the perception of cause and effect and further development of that which has been discovered by others will always remain new. Seneca, 4 B.C. - 65 A.D.

A note of warning should be given here with no intention of decreasing the initiative and freedom of the problem solver. There exists the problem of the crackpot or "Rube Goldberg" inventor. He attempts to solve insignificant problems arriving at solutions which were discovered long ago. In designing, we should select those problems which are of real and key value and which appear to be solvable within the time available and with the tools we have at our disposal. Each of us can sit down and list one-dollar, ten-dollar, one-hundred thousand dollar and million-dollar problems. We can also select one-person problems, ten-person problems, thousand-person problems. We should, especially if we are involved in a profit-making organization, select those problems of greatest value and those which will help the largest number of people.

Strange how prudent men cautiously walk into oblivion, while audacious men indiscreetly rush into immortality. Anon.

This requires a tremendous amount of creative insight. A study of history will quickly reveal that the truly creative solutions to problems were those which at first appeared to be impossible of solution, and of little significant value. In a current book it is difficult for the reader to reach any definite conclusions about how to separate the fantasies from the ideas which are remotely possible. Having lived through the age when space travel was transformed from fantasy to fact we have become more cautious in our evaluation of potential ideas.

Fads and Fallacies in the Name of Science, by Martin Gardner, who also wrote *Mathematical Puzzles and Diversions* (fascinating problems of mathematics).

SUMMARY

We must recognize that a "mess" exists, we must determine what questions should be answered. We may find such problems by studying the needs of mankind, by evaluating the deficiencies and assumptions of present solutions, by studying new ideas, and by developing a questioning attitude of constructive discontent.

A sample work sheet to use as a guide . . .

Design Work Sheet

RECOGNITION

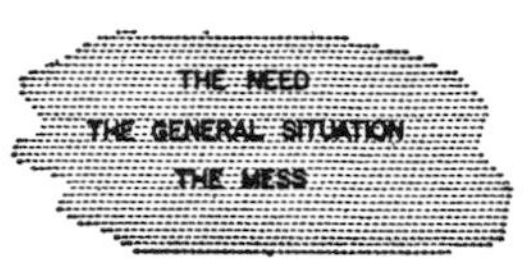

Describe the general situation or "mess" at the start of the problem.

What is the need that is to be satisfied in this problem?

What are the disadvantages of the present solutions to this problem?

What compromises have been made in present solutions?

Are these compromises necessary?

Can we improve the solution

- by increasing the design's function?
- by accomplishing the goal with a new approach?
- by making the design
  - longer-lived?
  - more accurate?
  - safer?
  - more convenient?
  - easier to maintain?
  - cheaper?
  - better appearing?

Can we reduce costs

- by eliminating parts?
  - substituting other materials?
  - revising methods of manufacture?
  - changing methods of assembly?
  - reducing labor?

Samples of Recognized Problems

The following problems resulted from analyzing mankind's needs. They come from *Inventions Wanted by the Armed Forces,* printed by the National Inventor's Council, and obtainable from the U.S. Department of Commerce:

1. **Freezing point measurement method** — a compact, accurate, rapid method for determining the freezing point of coolants in military equipment during Arctic operations. Equipment now in use is cumbersome and requires technical personnel to operate it. Desired equipment should be as easy to use as the conventional automotive hydrometer but of improved accuracy.
2. **Angle of attack** — a mechanism to measure angle of attack at hypersonic speed. It must operate at high temperatures and in a fringe of the earth's atmosphere.
3. **Altimeter** — pressure sensitive mechanisms for measuring pressure altitude to 500,000 feet or higher. Must be simple and generally suitable for installation on aircraft.
4. **Vibration isolation equipment** — devices are required which will preclude deleterious effects to sensitive airborne equipment which must function properly in high "G" environments and in severe vibration conditions. High fidelity of data from the basic sensor is required without attenuation of performance due to use of vibration isolation device.
5. **Self-restoral submarine cable** — when a break occurs in a submarine cable the section between repeaters shall disconnect and the remaining repeater terminals shall start producing sonic waves. A new cable section when put in the area with temporary sonic seeking torpedo type carriers shall connect the two end repeaters with the new cable section to restore electrical signal transfer.
6. **Anti-icing aircraft** — new chemical, mechanical or electrical ways and means of de-icing and anti-icing aircraft in flight.
7. **Rough terrain landing gear** — landing gear to permit short landing and takeoff aircraft to operate from unprepared areas, such as marshes, plowed fields and rocky surfaces. Must be lightweight.
8. **Retractable rotor systems** — a retractable rotor which will enable an airplane to take off vertically like a helicopter, then retract for forward flight.

The above inventions are desired by the government and their solutions are not yet available.

We might also recognize problems which exist by keeping up-to-date with the new developments of products and procedures for problem solution. Almost all the current technical magazines include recent developments in a particular field of interest. For the designer these might include *Machine Design, Product Engineering, Industrial Research, IBM Journal of Research and Development, Bell Telephone Magazine,* and others. From continued survey of the above sources and others, the engineer might recognize that these are available to introduce him to new problems: Free-piston engine, Sandwich paneling, Thermoelectron engines, Electroluminescence, Inertial guidance, Cryoton, Ferrites, Super or exotic fuels, Theory of games.

We might also uncover problems by mere speculation, and by asking ourselves the question, What would happen if? Such speculation indicates that we realize problems exist and that today's solutions have disadvantages. The following are illustrations of this approach. How about:

Throw-away, hand-cranked, one-use engines to be used at extreme cold temperatures.

An automatic stamp dispenser at supermarket cash registers to count out trading stamps.

An automatic program selector for TV to permit pre-selection of weekly programs in advance.

A pressure transducer with digital output to eliminate the need for analog to digital conversion.

Dry batteries with infinite shelf life operating some what similarly to instant charge wet cell.

A simple, lightweight, inexpensive device that indicates the maximum shock or vibration which has been encountered in the shipment of fragile items.

Some continuous casting process for steel and other metals.

Improved bonding of dissimilar metals and other materials for fabrication.

Or, what types of equipment would be desirable should we prove successful in developing automatic controls for steering and operating automobiles?

3.

Definition

WE HAVE NOW RECOGNIZED that a "mess" exists. We have determined a general problem area and recognized some of the problems that must be solved before we are satisfied. However, we cannot solve a mess—we must be more specific than that. If we have recognized a need for a new type of communication, we must now decide more specifically what these words mean, what specifications must be met before the solution is acceptable, and what specific problems will be solved on the way to success.

The creative man must have in himself the incentive and the self-discipline to do the thing that he sees needs to be done. Arthur Compton.

It is well to point out that the nature of the solution to the problem will depend upon our manner of defining it. Suppose you were given the following problem situation:

> An engineer boards the midnight train from Cleveland for an important conference in New York scheduled at 9:00 the next morning. He dons pajamas, slippers and dressing gown and steps into the next car looking for his porter. In the meantime, his sleeping car, containing all his clothes, is switched to another train.

How would you define this problem? If we define the problem as, *How can he retrieve his clothes?* we will arrive only at those solutions which satisfy this narrow definition. But we may creatively conclude that there is a larger and more inclusive problem. By asking ourselves the question, Why does he want his clothes? we might conclude that the definition is actually, *How might he be present at the scheduled meeting tomorrow morning?* or, *How might the information which he possesses be adequately presented to the appropriate people in sufficient time to take the necessary action?* There are many other ways of defining the problem and each one will be colored by the individual's own personality and experiences. The point to remember is, the definition should be made in the broadest possible sense. It should include every acceptable solution and yet be made in such a manner as to focus attention on the heart of the problem.

Just definitions either prevent or put an end to disputes. Emmons.

FORMULATE

After recognition and before searching for a solution it is necessary to formulate a clear, exact statement of the problem in familiar words and symbols. It is now necessary to isolate the problem from the general situation and to delineate its form. This definition should spotlight every aspect of the problem on which attention should be concentrated. The nonessentials should be stripped away and the individual characteristics of the problems should be differentiated. It should be determined whether or not the immediate problem is part of the larger problem. If it is, it should be determined what relationship exists to the total part.

Some years ago some researchers were presented with a problem situation involving the formation of ice on a television tower. The ice would form during certain types of weather, fall away from the tower, and cause damage to vehicles and people below. A general formulation of this problem might be, *How to prevent ice from forming on a television tower?* By asking such questions as, *What would happen if ice did form?* and, *What harm would such formation do?* It was determined that this first definition was much too narrow. A much broader definition was, *How to prevent ice which forms on a television tower from doing harm or damage to people and equipment below the tower?* It is significant to note at this point that as the problem was presented to the solver it was stated as, *How can I keep ice from forming?* It is quite possible that a new and unique definition will be required before this problem can be satisfactorily solved.

DIFFICULTIES OF FORMULATION

To DEFINE THE problem adequately is a difficult task. We must leave the beaten path in order to get a creative definition leading to a solution. Once the problem is adequately defined, we have come a long way toward solution. The task of definition is made more difficult because we are human beings psychologically influenced by our environment. Unless we are very careful in our thinking, our mental habits will become mechanized and rigid.

The Maier two-cord problem is a significant illustration of the psychological difficulties involved in problem solving. Students were asked to solve a problem for which there was a total of four possible solutions. Two cords were suspended from the ceiling of a room and the task was to tie the two together. One string hung near a wall and the other from the center of the room. The subject soon learned that when he held either cord in his hand he could not reach the other. He was told he could use anything

N. R. F. Maier, *Journal of Comparative Psychology,* **11:** 181-94, 1931.

in the room to solve the problem. The four possible solutions were (1) using a large object to anchor one cord while the other was brought to it, (2) lengthening one cord with an extension cord so as it could reach the other, (3) pulling one cord in with a pole while holding the other, and (4) attaching a weight to the center cord and then swinging it to reach the other cord. The last solution was the most difficult and was the object of the experiment. Of the students studied, 39% solved the problem without any hints; an additional 37% solved it after receiving hints; and 23% failed to solve the problem at all.

The experiment was then repeated with new subjects but this time a group of the subjects was first asked to solve another problem involving an electrical circuit and a switch, while a second group was asked to solve an electrical circuit problem using a relay. Then the Maier two-cord problem was presented. Of those subjects unhampered by a previous electric circuit problem there was only a chance relationship in the choice of the relay or the switch to serve as a weight to swing the center string. However, seven out of nine of those who had previously used the switch in the other problem used the relay in this one. In 17 out of 19 cases the object not previously used was used as a weight for making the center cord into a pendulum. When asked why they had chosen the object they did, the subjects provided rather defensive reasons (i.e., "anyone can see this is the better one to use," "this one was obviously much better"). It may be seen that a person is limited in his problem solving by his habits and by his previous solutions to problems.

Our doubts are traitors and make us lose the good we oft might win by fearing to attempt. Shakespeare.

We have difficulty in defining a problem also because of the way we see things. There is a story about a gentleman at a party who had had too much to drink. He noticed a very attractive woman across the room but when he came closer to her he noticed it was his mother-in-law. His problem solving was burdened by the way he saw things—failure of perception. Things are not always what they appear to be. This might be illustrated by another example. Some students were once given the task of removing a ping-pong ball from a rusty pipe that had been bolted upright to the floor. In the room with the pipe, students found hammers, pliers, soda straws, strings, pine, and an old bucket of dirty wash water. After fishing vainly with the various tools most of the students finally saw a solution; they poured dirty water into the cylinder and floated the ball to the top. Then the experiment was repeated on other students with one important change; instead of the bucket, there was a crystal pitcher of fresh ice water surrounded by shining goblets on the table with a gleaming white cloth. Not one student solved the problem because no one could connect the beautiful pitcher and its clean water with the rusty pipe.

It is necessary in defining the problem in its broadest sense to avoid the traps and blocks in our thinking brought about by our previous habits and by the previously successful solutions to problems. We must get away from the obvious, see behind the symptoms, to get at the basic difficulty.

TERMINOLOGY

In the proper statement of the problem we must be cautious to use familiar words and familiar symbols and to define all terms that might possibly be ambiguous. We must be sure that all the words and terms used are clearly and specifically understood. The problem solver is limited by the way in which he sees things. Familiar situations lead to past answers

People think that if they have a name for a thing, they understand it. Kettering.

to the problem. By conversion into familiar symbols it is possible to latch on to past ideas and solutions. The only real solutions we have for problems are those which come from past experience.

Language is only the instrument of science, and words are but the signs of ideas. Johnson.

Language is not only the vehicle of thought, it is a great and efficient instrument in thinking. Sir Humphry Davy.

Since past experiences are the raw materials for our solutions and since we live in a physical world and think in physical terms it becomes necessary to our problem solution to use models as an aid in our thinking. Our understanding of atomic matter was greatly faciliated by Niels Bohr who formulated a somewhat satisfactory model of atomic structure. While it was true that the analogy between the atom and the construction of the universe was not exact and led to erroneous conclusions, the physical model helped in thinking through the problem.

A good deal of difficulty occurred because Bohr hypothesized that the electrons were "going round" the heavy nucleus of the atom. Upon investigation of the words "going round" it was determined that this condition was satisfied if we could see an electron first at one position and then at another. This condition required that the electrons be emitting waves and it was concluded that such was not the case. The attempt to define these very simple and commonplace terms led to a deeper understanding of the real problem.

A similar difficulty occurred in the case of Einstein when he attempted to clarify the problem of light and relative motion. He concluded that he was not sure of the meaning of all terms and upon trying to define the terms in relation to his physical observations, he concluded that any event may be simultaneous to one individual attached to the earth but not equally simultaneous to another moving object. This, after much effort, led him to the conclusion that the speed of light must be the constant.

This is not just a game of "antics with semantics." It is necessary that we know specifically all the terms with which we are dealing or that we make suitable assumptions. In design we must decide what a ball bearing is in its most general terms. This may be defined as a device which will exert a force between members which are in relative motion. If we define a clutch as a mechanism which will control the flow of mechanical power we must be sure we understand the meaning of the word control. When the problem is defined in its broadest terms the number of possible solutions is substantially increased. A clutch is not only a device with shoes or bands but it may involve hydraulic, electric or acoustical mechanisms as well. A bearing is not just two members separated by balls or rollers but may involve dynamic or static fluid separation.

The difficulties of formulating a definition may be overcome if we are deliberately creative, and approach the problem with an open mind and a questioning attitude. These difficulties stem from our past experiences. These experiences may help us if we use them carefully and cautiously.

What is defeat? Nothing but education; nothing but the first step to something better. Wendell Phillips.

SUB-PROBLEMS AND SUB-SUB-PROBLEMS

THE PURPOSE of the general formulation, then, is to spotlight our attention on every aspect of the problem. It is an effort to make the general "mess" take form. To solve a complex problem as a whole is difficult, if not impossible. It becomes necessary to break the problem down into smaller quantities and sub-problems. These subdivisions should be as small as possible and in terms that we ourselves understand. Once the problem has been subdivided we can approach those problems which we believe are key factors and successively introduce more problems and more complexities into our solution.

As an example, we might decide to design a "hootenanny." Before we have a solution to the total problem we would have to solve such sub-problems as basic function, reliability, producibility, breakage and wear, maintainability, operation, and others. These then constitute sub-problem areas. The type of product involved will determine the relative importance of the various problem areas. The total solution of the problem will involve a balanced integration of all of the solutions to the sub-problems. Each of the problems are interdependent and each of the solutions will be interdependent.

A basis for evaluation of the solutions to these sub-problems is necessary. This will require us, then, to write specifications for what type or types of solutions will be acceptable to each of the problems. Some of these specifications must be classified as absolute and must be adhered to regardless of which solution is used. Other specifications can be called only desirable and will be incorporated into the solution as is possible. The total solution to the problem will be a compromise. No one solution will meet all the requirements set up for the problem. For each advantage there appears some disadvantage. It will be necessary at the evaluation stage to return to these specifications and determine the relative merits of each solution.

How little do they see what really is, who frame their hasty judgment upon that which seems. Southey.

A brief word about the nature of absolute specifications. A problem is proposed involving a small, valuable white mouse which is placed into a bottle. Over a period of time the mouse grows and its value increases. The problem then arises, how to remove the mouse from the jar, its head having grown too large to go through the jar neck. The difficulty is, we don't want to break the jar and yet we want to remove the mouse alive. How would you solve the problem? The solution is very simple—break the jar. No one would want to lose a very valuable mouse in an effort to save an inexpensive container. The point made here is that the specification that the jar not be broken is typical of many of the so-called "absolute" specifications which we impose upon ourselves in problem solving. It is well to investigate the wisdom of each of the specifications.

HOW TO DEFINE

Before an engineer can define the problem properly he must recognize all the problems that exist. Most of the failures in machines occur not because we make mistakes in analyzing the problem but because we fail to recognize that there is a problem. For example, the first-year maintenance cost for a paint-drying oven was $2,080—an oven whose original price was $1,700. The high cost was due to the frequent dismantling and cleaning necessary because of the oxidization of oil in bronze sleeve bearings mounted within the baking chamber. Once the problem was recognized the solution was relatively simple—mount the bearings outside the oven. In this instance, the designer failed to recognize that a problem would exist under these conditions.

In another case involving 200 vacuum pumps, excessive labor was involved to remove the crank case drain plug (located at the bottom of the machine base), for required frequent oil changes. This change required two men to disconnect, dismount, and raise each machine over a drain pan. The designer in this case failed to recognize that a problem would arise when the pumps were serviced.

In another case involving a gas-engine-driven centrifugal pump used for cleaning out pits, the hand-crank mechanism on the engine failed to disengage and broke the maintenance man's wrist. Once it was realized that a certain lack of reliability existed in all equipment and that in certain designs, lack of reliability can result in a safety hazard, it was concluded that all such equipment should be equipped with self-starters.

We must anticipate the problems which exist not only under normal use and operation but under conditions somewhat remote from day-to-day activities. Very often a good solution to a problem can fail because of some remote human difficulty. Take, for example, the plastic bags used to cover dry-cleaned garments. Serious difficulties have arisen because these plastic bags are being re-used for other purposes, such as crib mattress covers. Under certain conditions the bags become hazardous to life because of their ability to pick up static electricity. They have already caused the suffocation of many children. So it can be seen that solutions may fail because of serious problems which occur under conditions for which the product was not designed.

Once we have recognized all the problems which exist we should attempt to summarize in a concise statement what appears to be a single problem. For example, "The purpose is to ______." We should list all factors thought to have a bearing on the need. It may be necessary to reduce the problem into sub-goals and sub-problems. Such statements should be in simple elements and familiar symbols. We might list the difficulties as follows:

> To overcome the following obstacles ______. In such a way that ______(specifications of cost, size, weight, performance, minimum acceptable criteria).

We might ask ourselves a check-list as follows:

What are the limits of the problem?
What is only desirable?
What are we trying to accomplish?
What are the difficulties?
What is necessary?
What results are desirable?
What portion of the problem should be undertaken?

Sub-problems or specifications might be determined by the following check-list:

1. Normal function and performance
2. Legality—such as codes, governmental regulation and the like
3. Consumer specifications
4. Safety in operation, maintenance, shipping, such as failure of parts, vibration, noise and fumes
5. Convenience of operations
6. Life, including wear, lubrication and breakage
7. Material availability
8. Transportability
9. Rigidity
10. Cost, both initial and operational
11. Overload capacity, including shock loading conditions
12. Weight and size
13. Producibility
14. Maintainability
15. Appearance
16. Adaptability

For various products, these items assume various orders of importance. Usually some are absolute requirements and others are only relative and desirable. A balanced design will be one which is just good enough to meet all the necessary requirements. These specifications will be subject to constant reassessment and review. If the relevance of a factor cannot be immediately determined, consideration of the factor should be included for consideration rather than left out.

The limits imposed on the problems under the above problem areas constitute the specifications of the design. The specifications are desirable in order to "box in" the problems and to offer goals and boundary conditions. All too frequently these specifications are not known, in which case it might be desirable to assume some logical limits or to determine the implied limits before proceeding to the preparation stage.

SUMMARY

Having recognized the "mess," we must study the problem in detail. We must convert the basic problem and its sub-problems into familiar and specifically defined words. We must determine the confines or specifications of any solution which may be found.

The purpose of such definition is to guide the engineer in his preparation, analysis, and synthesis and to serve as the basis for the evaluation and selection of a final solution. This phase of the problem is extremely difficult and the highest degree of creativity is required to overcome our mental habits.

A sample work sheet to use as a guide . . .

Design Work Sheet

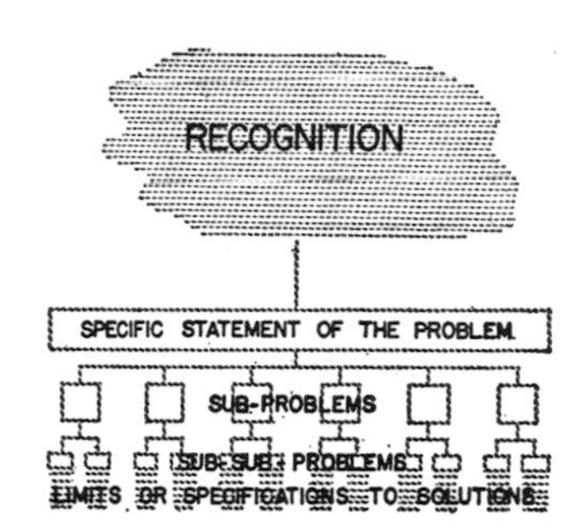

DEFINITION

The purpose of this design is to:

(Write in the simplest engineering terms and symbols with which you are familiar.)

To overcome the following obstacles or sub-problems:

In such a way that the following limitations or specifications will have been met:

Check-list of specifications:

normal function
reliability of function — wear, breakage, deflection, lubrication, heat
customer specifications
legality such as codes, regulations
operation — efficiency, reliability, safety
maintenance
shipping
producibility — methods, materials
cost — initial, operational
overload capacity — shock
adaptability
appearance
etc.

4.

Preparation

ENGINEERING PROBLEMS are solved by studying the data, and by studying, at the same time, the observations and solutions of earlier similar problems in the light of the current problem and its requirements. So we have a problem area which presumably has been studied in detail [Recognition], and the requirements and limitations set [Definition]. It is necessary now to accumulate all the materials out of which the solution may be fashioned [Preparation], and dissect this information into its basic components [Analysis].

The preparation stage should be so conducted as to make analysis as easy as possible. After the information is accumulated, it should be simplified to determine the component ideas involved. Then it may be reassembled or synthesized to put it into an effective form.

Science is always wrong. It never solves a problem without creating ten more. Shaw.

As solutions are attempted, it will be seen that some preparation is probably necessary even before the problem can be properly defined. And, some data may need to be analyzed before appropriate additional data can be collected. Thus we may conclude that this process is not simple and straightforward but involves continual redefinition, repreparation, reanalysis in order that we may be properly equipped to synthesize the solution. This points up the need for taking a flying start at any complex problem. In any problem we should try to start regardless whether the start is the wisest and most promising one we could make. As we continue to expand and penetrate the problem, our understanding of its deep implications increases and our efforts become more directed.

PROBLEM SOLUTION NOT STATIC

As WE STUDY history, we become aware that problem solving is not static. At any given time, certain facts, observations, methods, and materials are readily available to the solver and result in a given optimum solution. Later, one or more of these variables will change, demanding a revision of what we think is the optimum solution. We must realize that time is a variable in solving problems and that a solution will probably be most pertinent for only a short interval of time.

As new methods, materials, and ideas appear they will add to our perception of the problem. This requires a certain ability to work with facts and ideas realizing, all the while, that they are far from perfect. At the present rate of development of new ideas and methods, it is very important to run like mad in order to keep up with the world.

Some people study all their lives, and at their death they have learned everything except to think. Domergue.

FACTS - DATA

AN ESSENTIAL phase in the solution of a given problem is the accumulation of pertinent data. Such facts may be either qualitative or quantitative. The qualitative facts are usually obtained by observations which result in the comparison of one quantity with another. Such quantities may not be at their optimum con-

Science is organized knowledge. Herbert Spencer.

ditions nor is the relationship usually known between these two quantities and a third one. In general, the conditions under which such observations are made are uncontrolled and their pertinence or validity will be significant only in the light under which these observations are made.

These subjective facts are received by our senses—principally by sight. There is, therefore, a problem of perception (this problem is similar to the one experienced by the man and his mother-in-law). We do not always see what we think we see. What we see is colored by habit, by previous experiences, and by our opinions and attitudes. Furthermore, we must interpret what we observe in the light of other observations. It is essential that we receive these subjective "facts" with an open mind and try to avoid the various mental blocks which result in fixed and rigid thinking.

Certain other bits of information are in quantitative form, such as the temperature of a fluid, the strain at a given point, the hardness of a piece of metal, and the like. In such cases, some property of a process or material is converted into a measured quantity. This measured quantity may or may not have an exact relationship to the property desired. For example, we are not quite sure whether a Brinell hardness tester does measure the "hardness" of a material. Such an instrument measures the degree of permanent deformation of a material and this we name hardness. If we attempt to determine the "hardness" of a piece of steel and a piece of rubber, using this instrument, we would have to concede that the rubber is harder than steel.

Such a conclusion appears to be contrary to experience. However, for a given range of application we find such measurements extremely useful. Also, we find it impossible to measure the *quantity* "heat" but find it very convenient to measure the *effects* of heat.

The pertinency of the measured quantities to the problem is significant only to the extent that the problem matches the assumptions under which the observations were made. To the extent that we do not match the condition, we must make corrections or accumulate other data. We must creatively anticipate what the variables are in a given situation. It should be noted that such measurements are of little value by themselves but must be studied together with other bits of information to determine what relationships exist. Facts in themselves are useless and come to life only when arranged in a definite pattern.

PREVIOUS PROBLEM SOLUTIONS

Solutions come about largely by trial and error. In time, we ourselves, by our own actions or by studying the problems of others, build up a repertoire of successful solutions. If we are farsighted we will try to generalize from such successful adventures. The unsuccessful solutions are usually discarded and not attempted again. We should, however, creatively interpret such failures to determine the causes and to try to generalize the conditions under which they could be a success.

Just the minute you get satisfied with what you've got, the concrete has begun to set in your head. **Kettering.**

Difficulty arises when, upon meeting a new problem which is similar but not the same as a previous situation, we again attempt to use the old solution. Very often this results in failure since the conditions are now changed. If it is at all successful it rarely results in obtaining an optimum solution. If it fails we are confronted with a mental block since our generalization indicated that the solution was acceptable. We have difficulty in seeing these ideas in new situations.

We arrive at a further block in trying to solve a problem which already has a partial solution. It is a very easy habit to use an existing solution to the problem. We assure ourselves that there must be a logical reason for solving the problem as it has been solved. Certainly if there were a better solution someone would have thought of it by now. Certainly others are more capable.

Despite the potential danger it is well that we attempt to generalize conclusions from successful solutions. Such generalizations take the form of opinions, rules of thumb, and empirical relationships. Then, by analogy, we use these habits to solve problems. Also, on an unconscious level, these generalizations result in hunches, guesses, and "spontaneous" ideas. They also help in the periods of incubation and illumination during the process of synthesis which will be discussed later.

PREVIOUS ANALYTICAL PROCEDURES

NOT ONLY DO the solutions to previous problems become part of our preparation, but also the methods which were employed. Each of us attempts to transfer previously successful procedures to new situations. It would be folly and time-consuming if we insisted on developing new procedures for each problem. Some of the analytical procedures at our disposal have taken lifetimes to perfect.

Those analytical procedures of primary interest to a given class of problems are usually assembled under a common title. For example, the mechanical engineer solving problems involving energy and its applications to solids, liquids and gases is primarily interested in analytical procedures which come under the titles of mechanics, strength of materials, vibrations, thermodynamics, heat transfer, and metallurgy. By grouping these procedures under these general titles we have made these tools more readily available.

However, in other fields also we may find analytical procedures which are applicable and pertinent to the solution of a given problem. Such fields of study as psychology, sociology, geology and the like are fruitful as potential sources of creative solutions. There is therefore a deep need for understanding other fields of study, particulary those which fall under the heading of "liberal education."

Such analytical procedures result in generalities or laws. In the case of engineering in which we are analyzing quantitive data, these procedures result in equations and formulas. Such equations show the relationships which exist between various facts and observations. They do not result in an answer or a solution to a problem. They are valid only under the specific conditions under which the analysis was made. Furthermore each of these formulas was made for the specific assumptions and limitations imposed upon the procedure. Such assumptions are necessary in order to be able to physically execute such an analysis. Should we have included every variable in every analysis we would never arrive at a relationship. We should therefore not use equations and procedures blindly without thoroughly understanding the conditions under which these relationships were determined. If we decide that the use of such equations is justified by the time and accuracy available, we should be careful to adjust or correct for any significant deviations from these conditions. Stress concentration factors and other empirical and experimentally determined factors attempt to correct for such variations.

Such procedures and relationships are based upon some very generalized assumptions which, in general, we have no way of proving.

A detailed discussion of the relationships which result from these analytical procedures may be found in *Physical Laws and Effects* by C. F. Hix, Jr., and R. P. Alley. Some of these are as follows:

Ampere's Law
Archimedes Principle
Avogadro's Law
Bernoulli Film
Boyle's Law
Charles Law
Coulomb's Law
Curie-Weiss Law
Dalton's Law of Partial Pressures
Faraday's Law of Induction
Fick's Law
Gauss' Law
Gay-Lussac's Law
Graham's Law
Hooke's Law
Joule's Law
Jurin's Law
Kepler's Law
Kohlrausch's Law
Lambert's Law
Lenz's Law
Mariotti's Law
Newton's Law
Ohms' Law
Paschen's Law
Snell's Law
Stefan-Boltzmann Law
Stoke's Law
Weber-Fechner Law

There are, furthermore, certain cause and effect relationships or observations which may be useful for analyzing problems:

Barkhausen Effect
Bauschinger Effect
Bremstrahlung Radiation
Brownian Movement
Cavitation
Christiansen Effect
Compton Effect
Corbine Effect
Doppler-Fizeau Effect
Edison Effect
Electrodeposition
Electrostriction
Faraday Effect
Fission
Gauss Effect
Hall Effect
Hertz Effect
Nernst Effect
Pinch Effect
Poisson's Ratio
Radioactivity
Seebeck Effect
Stark Effect
Thermoelastic Effect
Volta Effect
Wien Effect
Zeeman Effect

It is significant to note from the above lists that for each of us there are a number of relationships and observations we are not acquainted with. This may mean that we are passing up potential tools for the solution of problems.

These analyzed relationships are basic ideas or concepts. To define clearly both the word *basic* and the word *concepts,* is very difficult. Each appears to be colored by individual experiences and attitudes. In general, these concepts have no real proof but represent a sort of common relationship between general classes of items. Each person will have his own list of basic concepts which is potentially available for the solution of all problems. By analogy, we may be able to apply the concept to the problem by adjusting the meaning of the variables.

The poverty of thought material is the chief characteristic of poor thinking. Karl Duncker.

MANNER OF OBTAINING THE PREPARATORY MATERIAL

THE MOST READILY available source of preparatory material is the individual himself. He is capable of receiving and storing a considerable amount of information over a significant period of time. In order to use such material the individual must possess self-confidence and self-reliance. As he begins to draw upon his own resources for solving these problems and acquire the necessary data he builds up confidence. To increase the usefulness of this source of information he must continually exercise his ability to observe and receive information, his facility to manipulate and combine and use this information, and his ability to try out ideas.

Thinking cannot be clear till it has had expression. We must write, or speak, or act our thoughts, or they will remain in a half torpid form. Henry W. Beecher.

He can also receive data and information from others in verbal or recorded form. Conversation is a source of observations and ideas but not a very reliable source for "facts." Information also comes from such diverse sources as lectures, television and radio, and records. In recorded form we usually select materials from textbooks and handbooks.

Other and perhaps more useful sources of information are available. Ideas and data may be found in general literature, such as history and philosophy, in technical magazines, magazines on current affairs and magazines of general interest. Reports of technical societies and research organizations afford an excellent source of up-to-date data.

In all this, there is the serious problem of communication. The information must be conveyed from one individual to another. The conveyance and reception of such information is modified by the environment in which it must live, and the experiences of both the transmitter and receiver. Communication is a complex problem. We must do our creative best to increase its reliability and effectiveness. In language itself we have a problem of semantics or word meanings. Words like *good, substantial,* and *easy* are subjective and colored by personal experience. Words like *computer* which cover a class of ideas are not necessarily specific and must be interpreted. Words like *entropy,* involving a concept, are colored by experience and observations.

Libraries are the wardrobes of literature, whence men, properly informed, may bring forth something for ornament, much for curiosity, and more for use. Dyer.

There is also the problem of reliability of information. Not all information which we receive is correct, not all is pertinent, not all is consistent. We therefore can see the need for very creative preparation and creative analysis of this data before it can be assembled into a solution.

ANALYTICAL TOOLS

IN THE PROCESS of analysis certain tools have proved valuable in breaking down data and finding relationships. Such tools then become part of the preparatory material and useful in the efficient solution of a problem. These tools will be discussed further under the next section. The degree of skill with which we can use the tools will be proportional to our familiarity with them and the degree to which they have become part of our habits.

CREATIVE PREPARATION

THE USE OF obvious tools and obvious data in obvious combinations will result only in a routine solution to the problem. The task in design is to search for remote data and observations and tools in order that we will get unusual and creative solutions. To do so we must develop in ourselves an inquiring and open mind, a passion for accuracy and honesty, and exacting standards, if we are to find significant information. We must be nonconformist and be willing to try things even though they have not been done before. And we must have the motivation and intense desire to succeed, a desire to continue toward a solution even though the path is not clear.

Fully to understand a grand and beautiful thought requires, perhaps, as much time as to conceive it. Joubert.

At each phase of the solution we are faced with blocks—rigidity in our methods, a fixedness in our thinking which limits us in the way we see things and the way we think things should be done. Such blocks are increased by lack of motivation, by emotion and stress.

SUMMARY

A tremendous amount of material to solve each problem is available to us. The problem is not a deficiency of material but too much material. We find it difficult to assemble and use such material. We find furthermore that there is a problem of reliably and efficiently acquiring such data.

Each of us generally uses very little of his potential ability to prepare. To become effective we must be-

come acquainted with all or at least more of the tools and information available. In order that we may arrive at a creative solution, we must conduct creative *preparation.*

We must continually exercise our ability to receive or observe data, *and continually* try to understand new analytical procedures.

A sample work sheet to use as a guide . . .

Design Work Sheet

PREPARATION

The following facts are known:

Speed
Torque — full speed
starting
H.P.
Type of motion
Direction of motion
Physical properties:
size
weight
Type of service
Type of environment:
temperature
corrosive conditions
abrasion
Manufacturing:
quantity
tools available
skills available

Other information:
text books
technical magazines
technical, society magazines
other current literature

Possible useful physical laws and effects

Possible methods of analysis

Other solutions in any way similar to this problem

Ideas

5.

Analysis

Also suggest studying *Engineering Analysis,* Ver Planck and Teare.

IT IS NOW NECESSARY to break down accumulated information to determine, item by item, its contribution to the whole problem. The collected data must be sorted, each item broken into its fundamental properties, tested as to its reliability, completeness, and pertinence. It is necessary to determine differences and agreements in preparatory material, cause and effect relationships, variations and patterns which might contribute to the synthesis of a solution. The information is of little use until the interrelationships among the various facts have been established.

A few design problems will illustrate the need for further analysis. Supposing an engineer has been given the bending strength of a specimen, the magnitude of the loads imposed, the method of load application, the method of manufacture of the item and similar information. By itself, such information is of little value in building a shaft or in determining whether a given shaft will be satisfactory. One of the analytical equations which may be used to combine these data is $S=MC/I$. If we conform to the assumptions which are necessary in the derivation of this equation it will permit us eventually to compare the calculated stress with the experimentally determined strength of the specimen. Such analyses will answer the question, Will the shaft break?

If a designer is given the temperatures of two surfaces, the surface conditions and finishes and the material composition of the surfaces, he cannot determine the adequacy of the heat transferred until he has analyzed the data. This he does by using the equations of heat transfer and making sure that he conforms to conditions necessary in the derivation of these equations. This he can compare either to the quantity which he knows he must transfer or to a situation whose answer is known. It therefore is quite apparent that before an adequate solution can be determined for a given problem the collected information must be studied in detail.

Facts are of primary importance when relationships existing among them are established. A construction of existing relationships puts facts and ideas in a form most readily available for future synthesis.

METHODS OF ANALYSIS

THE EVENTUAL goal of analysis is the comparison between the present situation and past experiences. By knowing the essential aspects of past problems and knowing which solutions were workable, the engineer may arrive at a fair approximation to a solution for the present problem.

A thought is often original, though you have uttered it a hundred times. It has come to you over a new route, by a new and express train of association. Oliver W. Holmes.

Let us suppose the design task is to determine the size and configuration of a shaft to prevent breakage. Since we do not have a satisfactory theory for predicting failure without resorting to experimental situations, the solution involves the calculation of a theoretical stress to be compared to an experimentally determined strength of the material. In order to make such a comparison, the conditions for strength and for stress must be equivalent in all significant ways or some correction must be included to adjust variations. Such analysis might be as follows:

1. Determination of any loads (forces, torque, moments) for an assumed manner and location of failure. This analysis is based on Newton's Laws and geometry, and is covered in kinematics and mechanics.
2. Conversion of these loads to stresses or strains. These procedures are usually covered in elementary or advanced strength of materials.
3. Corrections made for variations from assumptions such as stress concentrations, shock factors and the like.
4. Determination of maximum values of stress or strain (see combined stresses in strength of materials).
5. Conversion of stresses to loading conditions equivalent to those existing when experimentally determined values of strength were obtained (see theories of failure).
6. Comparison of the experimentally determined values of strength to the equivalent maximum values of stress by the use of factors of safety consistent with: the design information, a problem definition, and the assumptions which were made.

Other methods of analysis might be used. Usually we do not feel that the comparison of loads is as suitable as comparison of stresses. However, in the design of belts or anti-friction bearings, the comparison of loads proves the more satisfactory. Sometimes relationships between variables are not known and then the analysis must be more subjective as it is in the case of boundary lubrication.

Certain logical procedures will aid in establishing relationships between the variables. In the method of agreement, all of the circumstances leading to a given problem are studied to determine the one or more factors in common. This factor may then be the key to any possible relationships or must necessarily be satisfied in the solution to the problem. For example, Newton was concerned with the problem of determining the rules governing the motion of an object. He therefore studied various objects in motion—the falling of a terrestrial object, the motion of a heavenly body in space, and the possible motion of atomic-sized particles. He concluded that there was a commonness in these situations which might be explained by forces of attraction and repulsion. This resulted in his three laws of motion. In the establishment of the periodic table in chemistry, the common properties of the various elements were studied and arranged according to the similarity of their effects and reactions.

We can also determine interrelations by studying the differences which exist. If two sets of circumstances differ in one factor only, and one set containing the factor leads to the problem and the other does not, this factor may then be the cause.

A third method for determining any cause-and-effect relationship is the one commonly employed in experiments. If the variation of the intensity of one factor in a problem situation results in a variation in the effect, then that factor may be the cause in the problem. In the design of various elements we find that the equations are a mathematical expression of such cause-and-effect relationships. The study of what happens as a size, the material, load, or loading situation changes is essential before a satisfactory shaft may be synthesized.

TOOLS FOR ANALYSIS

A WIDE RANGE of tools is available for the designer. These tools facilitate the determination of any relationships which exist between the data. It is desirable that these tools become an intimate part of the designer since his degree of skill in their use is proportionate to his familiarity with them.

The most valuable tool which the engineer possesses is mathematical analysis. The various mathematical procedures permit the designer to manipulate measurable quantities by converting them into impartial, generalized symbols. These generalized ideas are then manipulated and studied by certain rules of logic and when the relationships have been determined, the quantities are returned to their original form. The conclusions which were based upon the general class may then be available for the specific problem at hand. While such analysis may lead at times to nothing usable, the methods are extremely useful since they permit the engineer to study the data without the psychological and semantic limitations present in the original situation.

Arithmetic, algebra, geometry, and trigonometry are basic to the engineer. Calculus may be used for the analysis of quantities which are continuously variable in magnitude. The various forms of differential equations permit the further study of relationships between such quantities. Analytic geometry serves as a tool for the study of graphic relationships. Laplace and other transforms permit the change from one system of symbols to another for the sake of simplicity or convenience of analysis. Vector analysis and complex numbers permit us to study those quantities which possess two measurable quantities such as magnitude and direction. Statistics permit us to analyze data which are multivalued with respect to a given variable. Dimensional analysis assists in the determination of the possible forms of any relationships which may exist between the variables. The theory of games is a new mathematical procedure in analysis of quantities influenced by human behavior.

As mentioned previously, experimental procedures are also available for analysis. Such experiments do not necessarily have to involve the quantities of direct concern in the design. The use of analogies has become a very valuable and powerful tool for the engineer. He may use an analogy between a sand heap and the strain existing in a certain plate. He may use an analogy between an electrical circuit and a mechanical or hydraulic situation, as he does in an analog computer. He may, furthermore, use empirical relationships or depend upon his intuition. The methods to be employed in a given case must be consistent with the state of the art or of knowledge. When more precise methods are not available the engineer must rely on more superficial methods.

In various fields these mathematical methods have been formalized. Such organized procedures assist in the efficient and accurate solving of a given problem. Thermodynamics is the study of the relationships which exist between variables in heat processes. Heat transfer is the study of relationships which exist in the transfer of heat, mechanics involves the motion of physical bodies, and strength of materials involves the relationships between loads and stresses. There are other organized analytical procedures as well. The solver must be ever-conscious of the limitations and assumptions which were necessary to the development of such formalized procedures and should not follow them blindly.

The use of analytical procedures merely results in dissected information. The result of such convergent thinking is a smaller quantity of data and an understanding of the relationships which do appear. This data and information must be assembled again by the process of synthesis into an actual solution for the problem at hand. This involves divergent thinking. Analysis is not sufficient for a solution. The analyzed data must be combined in an effective way.

See J. P. Guilford, "Creativity," *American Psychologist,* 5:444-54, 1950.

DIFFICULTIES IN ANALYSIS

A NUMBER OF difficulties are present in performing an analysis. Not all of the data collected are of equal value nor is all the information pertinent to the problem. Sometimes we include bits of nonessential information by impulse or habit or by failure to agree on the real meaning of the words. Given the following problem:

> A plane carrying officials of the United Nations ran into another airliner and crashed precisely on the border between France and Italy. The only means of reaching the crash scene was on foot over exceedingly rough terrain. The rescue teams realized removal of the bodies would be difficult. The problem seemed to be: according to protocol, should they bury the survivors on the French side, the Italian side, or precisely on the border? The final decision was not to bury them in any of the three places but to carry them out regardless of the difficulties. Explain their decision.

The clue to the answer, of course, lies in the incompatibility of some of the information. Since the problem involved "survivors" there was no problem of burying them. We have been considering information not pertinent to the problem. Likewise in design, we almost always have available information which has no relationship to the problem.

In order to analyze the data it may be necessary to synthesize an arrangement. In design it is often necessary to guess at the placement of the bearings, the types of gears and the like, before the various relationships between the variables become apparent by analysis. As the relationships become apparent it is usually necessary for the engineer to synthesize a new solution. However, this trial-and-error procedure improves our understanding of the situation and assists analysis.

The shortest way to do many things is to do only one thing at a time. Cecil.

We often have difficulty in seeing many variables at a given time. The human mind thinks out a problem in little pieces and finds it difficult to keep many items simultaneously in its consciousness. It therefore is desirable to solve problems by successive complexity. At first we may attempt to solve a problem by treating it as a very ideal situation as in the case of rigid bodies, static loads and the like. As we understand how a relatively few number of variables react with each other we may develop an understanding of what may occur when the number of conditions has been increased. The use of simplifying assumptions is not only essential for the average engineer but is common practice in scientific investigation. Carc must be exercised in eventually correcting for the differences between the assumptions and the actual situation.

The solution of these problems is also hindered by certain psychological difficulties. The way we analyze is dependent upon who we are and how we think by virtue of the training and experience we have had. Some individuals are able to analyze in very abstract symbolism as in the case of an electrical engineer. Other individuals require more physical things as in the case of the mechanical engineer. Some people are very adept at analysis with words while others better understand graphic symbols.

Often university training results in a negative approach to problems and a feeling that there is only one answer and one correct method of analysis. Each individual is limited by what he sees as fundamental or basic, by a desire to be completely logical. We are furthermore limited by the way we see things and the way we think things should be done. With our emphasis on physical things we seem to have great difficulty in really understanding wave mechanics. We have difficulty in understanding what friction is and what the purposes are of bearings and lubrication. Our previous habits result in rigid thinking and fixed methods of analysis.

CREATIVE ANALYSIS

THERE IS A real need for becoming creative in our analysis. We must get off the beaten path if we are to find obscure relationships between bits of data. Methods of analysis are not straightforward and they involve much speculation. Einstein could not have developed his relativity theory without creatively getting off the beaten path with respect to his concept of the speed of light. A tremendous number of analytical methods are available for our use if we can look in more remote places or in fields not normally associated with our field of endeavor. Norbert Wiener showed that much could be learned about control systems by understanding human beings. Von Neuman showed that much could be learned about the functioning of economic systems by the study of card games and the like. The need for creativity is as acute in analysis as it is in other phases of problem solving. In order to analyze a problem creatively, certain personal characteristics are important. These will be considered in detail later and will be mentioned only briefly here. The designer must have a willingness to take a chance, he must have high self-confidence and motivation and a high degree of persistence in his work. He must be constructively nonconformist and flexible in his thinking. He must be actively curious about the world around him and open to experiences. He must have a well-grounded knowledge of the fundamentals of engineering and must be able to simultaneously consider several ideas. He must have a tolerance for ambiguity—that is, an ability to work with information even though he doesn't know where it is taking him. He must, furthermore, be able to suspend critical judgment until everything is known about the problem. He must be able to think in images, in analogies and be able to toy with ideas. He must be honest with himself and able to evaluate the wisdom of his procedures and ideas.

Ability to think in Analogies . . .

"Where'd we get this new operator?"

SUGGESTIONS FOR ANALYSIS

Besides the foregoing analysis, the engineer may attempt the classification of information in order to get an understanding of the data. For example, if our task were to design a new car we might determine that a car, whatever its final form, should have the following classes of items: propulsion, a means of suspension while the car is in relative motion, a frame, a source of energy, a mechanism to join the source of energy to the propulsion system, controls, and protection of the occupant from his environment. If we have determined that this basically constitutes a car we can then search for existing solutions under the various classifications.

Tolerance of Ambiguity . . .

"Wow! That's what I call a set of curves!"

In the case of a pin setter, the various devices which may be essential to its satisfactory operation may be classified in a language which is independent of the type of mechanism used. We might classify the various parts of a pin setter then as follows: separation, alignment, orientation, elevation, triangulation, spot and respot, and the like. We could then proceed to determine devices which were in any way similar to the above mentioned categories. It is essential that each of the above terms be understood as completely and as basically as possible. This symbolic classification of functions has been used very successfully in the design and operations of computer mechanisms.

If an engineer is concerned with the manufacture of an item which has already been designed, he might classify his accumulated data under one or more of the following classifications: materials, skill of the workers, equipment, tools, scrap, materials handling, and the like. Each of these classifications might be subdivided into smaller and more basic units.

There are various devices which might be used by the engineer to facilitate the study of these categories. With only two classes of variables a matrix may be constructed to permit the study of all of the variations of each variable. Three variables such as size, shape, and material, may be represented as the dimensions of a prism. Beyond three variables, the task of physically representing these quantities is quite difficult. Furthermore, the number of combinations of variables rapidly becomes astronomically large. Other methods which attempt to systematize the analysis of such information are attribute listing, in which every conceivable attribute of the object or problem is listed, and input-output technique, in which the inputs and outputs of tentative solutions are recorded.

For example, if the reader were asked to list the uses for a common brick, he could list all the attributes or properties possessed by the brick such as size, shape, color, weight, hardness, crystalline structure, solubility, chemical properties and the like. He could then proceed to synthesize a solution to his problem by involving each of the properties previously listed, as will be discussed in the next chapter.

SUMMARY

The purposes of analysis are to decrease the quantity of data available and to study the relationships which exist between the various facts. To find a solution to the problem we must use our past experiences. To use these experiences we must find similarities and cause-and-effect relationships between the present problem and the past. To find such relationships we must make use of many tools available to us. Mathematics is perhaps the most valuable, but the engineer must learn also to use experiment and empirical relationships if necessary.

Such analysis will not necessarily lead to a solution to the problem. The designer must still build up a solution or a configuration from these analyzed facts. To find a satisfactory solution he must be highly creative and wary of the habits involved in perception and his methods of thinking.

A sample work sheet to use as a guide . . .

Design Work Sheet

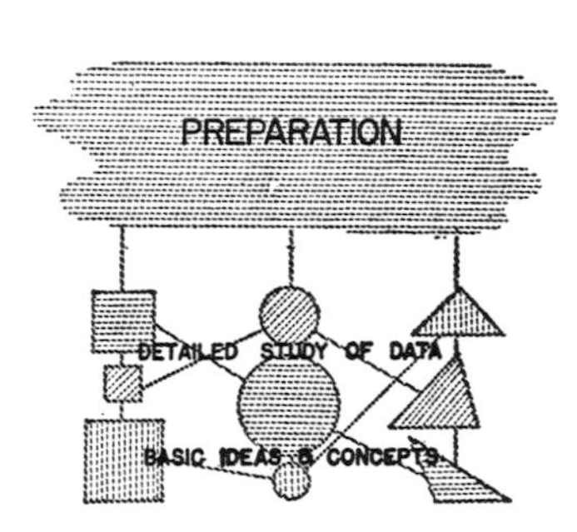

ANALYSIS

General methods of analysis

Assumptions

Detailed analysis, step by step

6.

Synthesis

THE WORK UP TO THIS POINT has been involved in two areas of interest. *Recognition* and *definition* involve the close study and picking apart of the problem itself. *Preparation* and *analysis* involve the close scrutiny and dissection of the potential raw material for a solution. It is now necessary to bring these two areas of interest together and to build up and *synthesize* a solution. To find some relationship between the problem itself and the collected information we must be divergent in our thinking.

The work prior to synthesis suffices to break apart and study both the problem and the information in an effort to bring the areas of interest as close together as possible. Synthesis is the making of a bridge joining these two areas. The narrower the gap between the two the easier it will be to construct the bridge.

As an example, suppose we desire to design a vehicle. As part of the problem area, we would determine the true nature of the problem and any requirements of the potential solution. We would collect information and analyze it to determine what the essential components of such a vehicle would be.

Then, keeping in mind simultaneously both the problem and the information we would attempt to solve one essential aspect at a time. Let us suppose we had to determine that one necessary part of the vehicle would be a means of suspension while the object is in relative motion. The designer would then think of devices and means of accomplishing this goal, thinking of all possible situations in any way connected with the above statement. He might think of skis, wheels of various shapes, fluid suspension, track-laying devices, magnetic and electrical suspension, and perhaps some solid type of bearing. This joining together of the problem with potentially satisfactory solutions, is the process of synthesis.

Great Design Ideas: The Wheel

Design News

The building up of solutions is accomplished by associating ideas. The operation of the human mind in the performance of this task is rather difficult to understand and relatively little is known about it. It involves the functioning of the subconscious mind which will be discussed later. Certain conditions foster, while certain other conditions hinder, the process. The engineer must simultaneously bring together both the problem and the pertinent facts. The rules of association were put forth long ago by Aristotle and are: similarity, contrast, and contiguity. Similarity involves the finding of some sameness of properties in two physical things or situations. Contrast involves an association because of differences in properties. Contiguity involves relating, or associating two objects or ideas by virtue of their physical placement.

An idea may be quite insignificant but it may acquire importance from an idea which follows it; perhaps, in a certain collection with other ideas, which may seem equally absurd, it may be capable of furnishing a very serviceable link. Morris Stein.

The association of ideas is most easily understood by thinking of various word association tests. In these the individual is asked to record other words which are brought to mind by a given word. Intuitively we tie together the various properties connoted by the original word with some other object. If you were given the word *mother,* you might think of *father* by the similarity of parenthood, or think of *father* by the contrast of sex, or think of *child* by the contiguity in childhood situations. As an engineer if you were given the word *shaft,* you might also think of the word *rod* or *round* by similarity of shapes. By the contrast of shape, the shaft would bring to mind such differences as *cubes* or *spheres.* By the process of contiguity you might also think of *bearing,* since we often see shafts and bearings together.

The process of association is also apparent in everyday life by the figures of speech and the phrases which we use. We speak of peaches and cream, bread and butter, black and white, fresh as a daisy, cool as a cucumber, and other phrases. Humor is dependent upon the use of idea associations.

Here is an example of how the solution of design problems also involves the association of ideas. Suppose you were given the assignment of transferring heat from one area to another in a clothes dryer. You would, by way of preparation, understand the various principles of heat transfer such as convection, conduction and radiation and the amount of heat which may be transferred in a given situation in each manner. By synthesis you would attempt to associate the requirements and the analyzed data with methods of accomplishment. You might ask yourself the question, Where else is heat transferred? You might then by some association think of such objects as stoves, refrigerators, clutches and brakes, and others. Each of these heat situations possesses certain peculiar properties which might be varied or assembled in various manners to solve the given problem. The designer might attempt to use the rotation property of clutches and brakes to produce an effective rotary heat transfer unit.

Instinct is probably the essence of past experience and knowledge stored up for later use. Henry Ford.

PROCEDURES OF SYNTHESIS

THE SMALLER THE gap that exists between what is known and what is to be attained, the easier it will be to build a bridge. In analysis it was suggested that the various properties of a given item be listed and classified. If you were to determine the various possible uses for a brick you might list every conceivable property which a brick possesses as follows:

size—height, length, width, weight, volume
shape
position, location, arrangement
strength
composition, ingredients
hardness
color
psychological effects
stability
adhesion and cohesion
heat properties—retension, absorption, transfer
crystalline structure
lack of ductility
time properties—speed, frequency tempo
energy and power properties
electrical properties
transmissibility of energy—acoustical, electrical, mechanical.

We might, furthermore, attempt to list these and innumerable other properties under one or more of the following categories: mechanical, electrical, hydraulic, chemical, acoustical, and others.

We would then try to apply this process of association to the mental manipulation of these various properties in order to uncover various possible solutions to the problem. Using association by contrast we might try to *change,* to *substitute,* or to *adapt* one or more physical properties. Using the similarity of association we might try to *combine,* to *merge,* to *add,* or to *find some other ingredient.* Other mental manipulations would be as follows:

transpose
reverse
magnify
subtract
minify
duplicate
separate
vice versa
upside down
exaggerate
omit
less of
copy
interchange
multiply
increase
shrink
condense
divide

Using these more detailed divisions of the general categories of similarity, contrast, and contiguity we might arrive at the following start of a list for the uses of a brick: building material, weight, weapon, counterbalance weight, border for ornamentation, support under object, step, grinding compound, anchor, warmer, scale for measuring, filler, hammer, grind-up for coloring, book end, straight edge, or spacer, insulation, break windows, part of a bookcase, anvil, toy, remold into objects, carve into objects, throwing device, as a shotput, model for painting, hardness gauge, cover, cooking device, comparison for color, cigarette support, advertisement. These answers are listed with the most common response coming first and the least frequent last. No attempt has been made to evaluate the wisdom of each suggested application.

Great Design Ideas: The Lever

Design News

The purpose of the preceding list is to assist in deliberately thinking of possible solutions to a given problem. The routine answers will come easily by associating commonly-experienced properties and objects. The clever and creative solutions will be achieved only by associating more remote situations and objects.

Many examples can be listed to show how association principles have been applied to solve everyday problems. The following list is but introductory and the reader is encouraged to add to it:

> ball point pen became a roll-on deodorant; throw-away papers became the basis of throw-away toweling, throw-away cartons, throw-away razor blades; combination of sweetened popcorn and toy became the present-day cereal box; wrist watches became wrist radios; rechargable car batteries became rechargable flashlight batteries; parallel railroad tracks may have been forerunner to parallel electrical wiring; light bulbs became flash bulbs; bullets became cartridge-type pens and grease guns; tires with tubes became tubeless tires; sawdust keeping ice frozen during the summer became basis for household insulation; heating in winter became cooling in summer; self-service cookie box became self-service store; peanut machines became cigarette, stamp and insurance vendors; the flatiron became the electric iron which became the steam iron.

In fields more intimately connected with engineering we may find the following:

> Archimedes solved his famous problem by substituting water for the mass of gold whose authenticity he was testing; different combinations of materials became new alloys; the adding machine became the computer; the hand sickle became the combine; low voltage car wiring became low voltage home wiring; flexible hose became flexible piping; electrical switchboards became hydraulic switchboards; pulley clothes lines became the dial mechanism of radios; pumps were fashioned after the human esophagus; computers fashioned after the human nervous system; jet engines fashioned after 12th Century Chinese rockets; bearings fashioned after the wheel; torque converters from pumps; multiple circuits for reliability from the idea of a spare tire; two windshield wipers from association by multiplication; miniature communication equipment, minify; automatic control systems, imitate human behavior; unit diesel injectors, separate injection of fuel from pump; incentive pay, rearrangement of pay; airplane pusher propellers, reverse.

DIFFICULTIES OF SYNTHESIS

In performing this task of tying together our knowledge with the problem at hand we encounter certain blocks which will be discussed in greater detail later. These blocks tend to prevent us from finding worthwhile solutions and they result from the way we see things, what we think things should be used for, and the way we think things should be done. These are all affected by our emotions, our motivations, and our entire psychological nature. These blocks may be classified as perceptual, or the way we see things, cultural, or the way we react to things, and emotional, or the way we feel about things. They are the result of our habits. The effect on synthesis by the way we see things, is illustrated by the Maier two-string problem discussed previously: previous use of one of the objects in another type of problem produced a mental block so that the solver could not appreciate that the device also possessed the property of mass. We must not let force of habit hinder us in searching for solutions. If we realize that these blocks exist we can consciously attempt to overcome them.

Another difficulty encountered by the solver is the problem of premature evaluation. If, in searching for a solution, another person were to evaluate and to criticize the wisdom of each suggestion, we would soon give up trying to find a solution. Likewise with our individual problems, if we immediately attempt evaluation and criticism for each idea, we will soon be discouraged in the search for better ideas. It is essential that we postpone the evaluation of any idea during the ideation stage, recording each and every idea as we find it and using each as a stepping stone for finding others. This is a process popularly called "brainstorming" in which no evaluation is permitted and the individual is encouraged to build upon previous suggestions. This technique may be used either individually or in groups with significant success. As various ideas develop they gradually approach uniqueness and become of potentially greater value.

It hinders the creative work of the mind if the intellect examines too closely the ideas already pouring in. Morris Stein.

Our fluency of ideas is greatly affected by a fear of making mistakes. Afraid of being wrong, we avoid even tackling the problem. Desire for security tends to make us fear the criticism of our fellow man. We therefore attempt only those tried things which minimize our errors—but this lack of daring also results in conformity and mediocrity. As a person's stake in life grows, as his potential loss in case of failure increases, he becomes more and more conformist and resistant to change. In all our actions and decisions we then desire to be "logical."

A new idea is delicate. It can be killed by a sneer or a yawn; it can be stabbed to death by a quip and worried to death by a frown. Brower.

Each of us must do his utmost to make sure he himself is not the stumbling block in the way of solutions. Often we are distracted by the values of others and this causes us to discard our own goals and ideas. The hard mental effort required to make our "dreams come true" is replaced by wishful thinking. We then become a part of the age of the great "goof-off"—the age of mediocrity.

It cannot be emphasized too highly that the designer has *responsibility* to innovate. The results which are truly worth while, which lead to progress—are those which are clever and creative and which are the result of leaving the beaten path. They will not come easily. The prevailing conditions all operate to produce routine answers. But these difficulties can be overcome, using techniques which are available—such as forced relationships, brainstorming, in-put out-put, and attribute listing—and these will help the designer to systematically and deliberately overcome the difficulties.

Incubation . . .

"It's driving me crazy! I simply can't stop thinking."

INCUBATION, ILLUMINATION

THE PROCESS of association is not always allied with conscious thinking. We often find the solution when we are not really thinking about the problem. This is called illumination. It is the sudden flash of insight, the "eureka feeling." Illumination follows a period of incubation during which time we are not consciously thinking about the problem.

Many people have written about this process and surely it has occurred to each of us on various occasions. The following quotations will illustrate this phenomenon:

See Ch. III, "Mathematical Creation" in *The Foundations of Science,* George Halsted (trans.), 1913.

H. Poincaré. Most striking at first is the appearance of sudden illumination, a manifest sign of long, unconscious prior work. The role of this unconscious work in the mathematical invention appears to me to be incontestable.

Carl Gauss. Finally, two days ago, I succeeded, not on account of my painful efforts, but by the grace of God. Like a sudden flash of lightning the riddle happened to be solved. I myself cannot say what was the conducting thread which connected what I previously knew with what made my success possible.

Does it not frequently happen that the name of a person or a place which you have in vain tried to remember, recurs to you when you are no longer thinking of it?

I allude to the familiar fact of recognizing a human face. Identifying a person you know requires the help of hundreds of features, not a single one of which you could explicitly mention. Nevertheless, all these characteristics of the face of your friend must be present in your mind—your unconscious mind, of course—and all of them must be present at the same instant. Therefore, we see that the unconscious has the important property of being manifold; several and probably many things can and do occur in it simultaneously. This contrasts with the conscious ego which is unique.

When I pronounce one sentence, where is the following one? Certainly not in the field of my consciousness, which is occupied by sentence number one; and nevertheless, I do think of it, and it is ready to appear the next instant, which cannot occur if I do not think of it unconsciously.

Often they [the ideas] *were there in the morning when I awoke . . . but they liked especially to make their appearance while I was taking an easy walk over wooded hills in sunny weather.* Helmholtz.

Francis Galton, 1908. When I am engaged in trying to think anything out, the process of doing so appears to me to be this: The ideas that lie at any moment within my full consciousness seem to attract of their own accord the most appropriate out of a number of other ideas that are lying close at hand, but imperfectly within the range of my consciousness. There seems to be a presence-chamber in my mind where full consciousness holds court, and where two or three ideas are at the same time in audience, and an ante-chamber full of more or less allied ideas, which is situated just beyond the full ken of consciousness. Out of this ante-chamber allied to those in the presence-chamber, ideas appear to be summoned in a mechanically logical way, and to have their turn of audience.

James Watt. I had gone to take a walk on a fine Sabbath afternoon. I had entered the Green and passed the old washing house. I was thinking of the engine at the time. I had gone as far as the Lord's house when the idea came into my mind that as steam was an elastic body it would rush into a vacuum, and if a connection were made between the cylinder and an exhausting vessel it would rush into it and might there be condensed without cooling the cylinder. I then saw that I must get rid of the condensed steam and injection water if I used a jet, as in Newcomen's engine. Two ways of doing this occurred to me: First, the water might be run off by a descending pipe, if an offlet could be gotten at a depth of 35 or 36 feet, and any air might be extracted by a small pump. The second was, to make the pump large enough to extract both water and air . . . I had not walked farther than the Golf house, when the whole thing was arranged in my mind.

See *James Watt,* by Andrew Carnegie.

The best current explanation of this process appears to be as follows: A person attempts to solve a problem by consciously preparing, analyzing, recognizing, and defining. He then attempts to synthesize solutions, trying various combinations and associations with little success. He then puts aside the problem and eliminates it from his conscious thinking. The subconscious mind, however, continues to work on the problem, associating ideas in various combinations. Various oral and visual stimuli tend to influence its functioning. The subconscious tries discarding those combinations which are not useful. The successful ones are brought to consciousness with a very exhilarating feeling of eureka. This process is very rapid, not being limited by time considerations as is the conscious mind. This process follows only after the periods of intensive and deliberate preparation, analysis, and definition have been completed. The solution appears suddenly and complete, devoid of any details. The person then has the

Happy ideas come unexpectedly without effort, like an inspiration. But they have never come to me when my mind was fatigued or when I was at my working table. Helmholtz.

feeling that "this is it," and feels assured that the solution will work.

Ah, I have found it. Archimedes, 287-212 B.C.

To use and encourage this process we must think extensively and intensively about the problem to be solved. We must deliberately attempt to solve it to the very best of our ability. However, if we are unsuccessful we should put it aside until a later time. We may then do something completely different and relaxing, such as taking a walk or playing a game. We may further encourage the process by trying to understand our own habits of thought fully, and the times and conditions under which we do our best thinking.

An idea, like a ghost, according to the common notion of ghosts, must be spoken to a little before it will explain itself. Dickens.

The greater the number of ideas, the greater will be the number of creative solutions. It has been found that the proportion of creative to noncreative ideas is constant for various individuals. The creative person merely thinks up a greater number of possible solutions.

A check-list for association:

likeness
difference
contiguity
sequence
cause and effect
combination
similarity
oppositeness
difference
vice versa
pattern
interchange
multi-use
other ingredient
other power
other process
merge
why
when
how
what about
what else
add
multiply
magnify
shrink
who else
where else
change pattern
  sequence
other layout
transposed
other causes
subtract
more time
strength
frequency
higher
wider
longer
ingredient
duplicate
exaggerate
minify
omit
tempo
opposite
switcheroo
upended
other end
divide
condense
lower
separate
less weight
faster
fewer parts
eliminate objectionable
rearrange
understatement
substitute
transposing use
unexpected combination
  (materials and ideas)

Great Design Ideas: The Ball Bearing

SUMMARY

Synthesis is a process of associating various properties and ideas with the problem at hand. The use of check-lists and various other techniques has proved very helpful in encouraging associations. The designer must avoid premature evaluation which might stifle the flow of ideas. To find a solution we must force ourselves to begin with relatively simple, common, and known associations. These may be used as building blocks for further efforts.

A sample work sheet to use as a guide . . .

Design Work Sheet

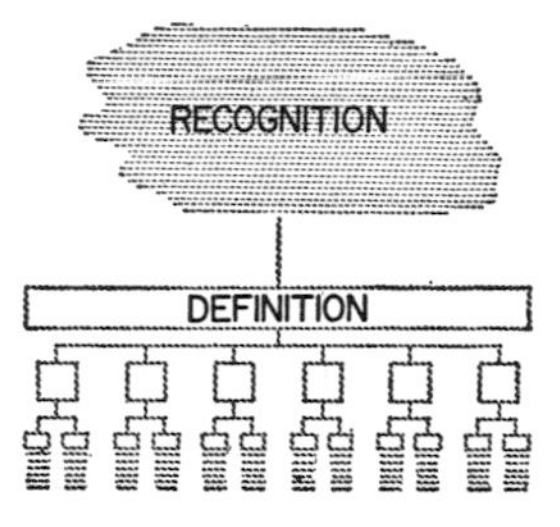

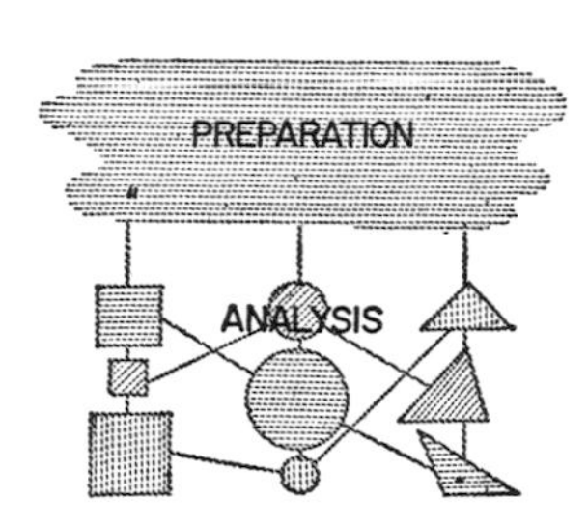

SYNTHESIS

What tentative solutions can be suggested between the analyzed information and the specific problems?

What variables exist that may be manipulated for a solution by transposing, reversing, exaggerating, separating? (See check-list p. 102.)

What configurations can be built using these variables?

What similar problems exist in other areas whose solutions may help?

What differences exist between such problem areas and this one?

What other problem areas exist in which the information and variables are similar?

The following are tentative solutions:

7.

Evaluation

When we complete analysis and synthesis we will have, if fortunate, a number of solutions to our problem. We have already determined by analytical means that these solutions are workable by comparing them with known solutions to similar problems. When each solution was first synthesized it was void of details. These details have now been filled in and we are ready to evaluate and select one or more solutions.

Two points must be made before proceeding with the discussion of the methods of evaluation. It is usually possible, quite contrary to our experience in course work, to have more than one answer to a given problem. There is not necessarily one correct answer to a given problem. This pursuing of alternate answers is often done in design situations. In the design of guided missiles, as well as atomic reactors, it was necessary to accept as possible solutions a number of arrangements of parts. We find that acceptable solutions differ largely because of the assumptions made and the interpretation of what the problem really is. It is possible that the final solution to the problem will be a combination of the solutions discovered. Finally, making a decision involves compromise. For every advantage there appears to be some price to pay. It is our objective to maximize the advantages in a given design and to minimize the disadvantages.

Whatever the solution we finally decide upon for a given design, it must be coordinated and balanced. The solutions to all the sub-problems must be combined to produce a maximum degree of benefit. On the other hand, a design must be just good enough. To design a machine to last a hundred years when it will become obsolete in ten is a waste of materials, time and skill. "Do not tie up a rowboat with a three-inch hawser." Our ideal should be the parson's one-horse shay in which all the parts managed to fail at the same time.

Evaluation is a critical study of the solutions in the light of the problem definition. It is necessary that we investigate each solution to each sub-problem and to compare them in all possible combinations. A number of criteria and a number of methods are available for such a study.

After all possible solutions have been determined, a very critical and detailed study should be made of their practicality and feasibility. Each idea should be investigated for its soundness. Potential responses and values should be studied together with probable satisfactions. Each idea should be compared with others as to its advantages and disadvantages. A comparison should be made with the original problem definitions. Our eventual goals should be to winnow the lesser solutions and, for those remaining, provide some means of selection.

A study should also be made of all the compromises thought necessary at various stages of the solution. All the assumptions should be investigated to determine whether they are logical and consistent.

Before proceeding to the selection a check should be made of all the work. All ideas should be logical and consistent with experience. If heat is to be dissipated, how does this amount compare to similar situations? All the analytical procedures should be checked for their pertinence to the problem and for any simplified assumptions made in any equations. A check should also be made concerning the consistency of ideas, the solver being very cautious about any which do not fit with the others.

Other important and often neglected aspects of evaluation are interpreting results and drawing conclusions. The solution to the problem immediately at hand is but part of the task. For the designer to grow and increase in ability he must consistently attempt to extend his understanding from the special to the general case. He should study those ideas which were rejected in the hope that much might be learned for the future.

METHODS OF EVALUATION

Before discussing the actual method it should be noted that whatever method is finally employed the task of evaluation is a difficult one. It is difficult because it involves our human behavior and our relationships with other people. We are sure that each time we make a decision someone else will judge our judgment. And yet we are faced with the task of deciding and having to make compromises. We are faced with a common desire for security, a desire to be logical, and a desire not to be wrong. Also, the excitement of finding a solution has now all but vanished and what remains is exceedingly hard and tedious work.

It is with our judgments as with our watches; no two go just alike, yet each believes his own. Pope.

What really complicates the decision is the fact that the problem is dynamic and not static. Things continually change. From the time the design has been initiated, the goal, the data, our viewpoint, and our knowledge have all changed. From day to day, the organization's goals will have changed in emphasis. When budget time comes around the emphasis is on money. When sales are slow, management becomes concerned with disposing of a large inventory. When we are quite busy we are anxious to solve each problem quickly. When the pressure is off, we are more willing to look ahead and determine longer-range objectives. In the long run, too, the problems change. Not only does the state of the art and human understanding of the problems change but the nature of the problems also changes. Management in a certain corporation, for example, after years of million dollar profits, may no longer find such profits satisfactory. Another company, after years of trying to obtain 10% of the market and failing, may find their 10 or 15% market expectation no longer reasonable. It is in these changing conditions that a decision must finally be reached. It must be made with full recognition of the fact that tomorrow a different answer may be more suitable.

A number of schemes may be used for evaluating the solutions. A check-list is perhaps the most common and usually takes the form of questions to be answered. Several check-lists are shown on following pages.

CREATIVE EVALUATION CHECK-LIST

Questions to help "measure" ideas:

1. **Is your idea simple?**
   Does it seem obvious? Or is it too clever? too ingenious? too complicated?

2. **Is it compatible with human nature?**
   Could your mother, the man-next-door, your cousin, the service station attendant all accept it?
   Is it direct and unsophisticated?
3. **Can you write out a simple, clear, and concise statement of it?**
   Can you do this in two or three short paragraphs so that it makes sense?
   Can it be understood and worked on by people of average intelligence?
4. **Does your idea "explode" in people's minds?**
   Does someone else react to it with, "Now why didn't we think of that before?"
   Do people accept it without lengthy explanation?
   If it does not explode, are you sure you have really simplified it?
5. **Is it timely NOW?**
   Would it have been better six months or a year ago? (If so, is there any point in pursuing it now?)
   Will it be better six months from now? (If so, can you afford to wait?)

Questions that can improve ideas:

1. **What is the simplest possible way of doing it?**
   If a seven-year-old boy were tackling the problem for the first time, how would he approach it?
   List on a sheet of paper every part or factor of your idea. Then ask of each part: Is this absolutely necessary?
   Are you sure you are starting fresh?—or are you being inhibited by customs, traditions, and "the way we've always done it"?
2. **Suppose the whole thing were completely reversed?**
   What new possibilities does this open up?
   What restrictions does it remove?
3. **Can public (or management, or employee) acceptance be measured?**
   Can you check the feasibility out "where life is going on"?
   Can you learn anything you ought to know by *asking* the public?

4. **What opportunities are being overlooked because no one has bothered to develop them?**

    Have you overlooked "the invisibility of the obvious"?

    What is commonplace in the idea? Can it be improved?

5. **What are the special needs of the situation?**

    Does the situation itself dictate idea specifications?

    Are there situation needs that haven't as yet been expressed?

    Will your idea satisfy the needs of the problem? If not, how could your idea be modified to strengthen it?

HOW TO EVALUATE POTENTIAL SOLUTIONS

1. **IDEA** Describe the potential solutions. Group and categorize the ideas				
2. **IDEA** Describe the potential solutions. Group and categorize the ideas	**REVISIONS** List necessary revisions. Strike out any impossible or undesirable ideas			
3. **IDEA** Describe the potential solutions. Group and categorize the ideas	**REVISIONS** List necessary revisions. Strike out any impossible or undesirable ideas	**ADVANTAGES** List advantages and estimate benefits. If no significant ones are evident, eliminate the idea		
4. **IDEA** Describe the potential solutions. Group and categorize the ideas	**REVISIONS** List necessary revisions. Strike out any impossible or undesirable ideas	**ADVANTAGES** List advantages and estimate benefits. If no significant ones are evident, eliminate the idea	**DISADVANTAGES** List disadvantages. If greater than the benefits, eliminate the idea	
5. **IDEA** Describe the potential solutions. Group and categorize the ideas	**REVISIONS** List necessary revisions. Strike out any impossible or undesirable ideas	**ADVANTAGES** List advantages and estimate benefits. If no significant ones are evident, eliminate the idea	**DISADVANTAGES** List disadvantages. If greater than the benefits, eliminate the idea	**FURTHER STUDIES** Study and combine remaining ideas. Investigate thoroughly, develop ideas completely, interpret the solutions, anticipate difficulties

EXAMPLES OF EVALUATIVE CRITERIA LISTINGS

U. S. Air Force "Key Criteria":

IS IT SUITABLE? Will this solution do the job? Will it remedy the problem situation completely, or only partially? Is it a permanent or a stop-gap solution?
IS IT FEASIBLE? Will it work in actual practice? Can we afford this approach? How much will it cost?
IS IT ACCEPTABLE? Will the company president (or the board, or the union, or the customers) go along with the changes required by this plan? Are we trying to drive a tack with a sledge hammer?

U. S. Navy Criteria Listing:

1. Will it increase production—or improve quality?
2. Is it a more efficient utilization of manpower?
3. Does it improve methods of operation, maintenance, or construction?
4. Is it an improvement over the present tools and machinery?
5. Does it improve safety?
6. Does it prevent waste or conserve materials?
7. Does it eliminate unnecessary work?
8. Does it reduce costs?
9. Does it improve present office methods?
10. Will it improve working conditions?

The "WORTH" method:

As your *first* evaluative step, ask and answer this question about every idea on your list:
"How much will it be *worth* if it can be made to work?"

Rotary International "4-way test":

Is it the TRUTH?
Is it FAIR to all concerned?
Will it build GOODWILL and BETTER FRIENDSHIPS?
Will it be BENEFICIAL to all concerned?

Look for improvements or developments:

What is the simplest way of doing it?
Is this (part or factor) absolutely necessary?
Are you sure you were starting fresh?
Suppose the whole solution were completely reversed?
Can public (or management, or worker) acceptance be measured?
What opportunities are being overlooked because no one has bothered to develop them?
What are the special needs of the situation?

EVALUATION OF IDEAS

Ideas by General Categories	*Evaluative Criteria*					*Decision*			
Categories	1	2	3	4	5, etc,	Use Now	Hold	Modify	Reject
A.									

EVALUATION OF REJECTED IDEAS

Rejected idea	What it suggests (How modify to make usable)
1.	
2.	
3.	

Several difficulties arise in using such lists. A check-list appears to be more satisfactory in eliminating unsatisfactory ideas than in finally selecting the best compromise. Certain items in the list usually have greater importance than others and are more likely to be the key to the solution. The check-list gives little indication of the relative importance of each consideration.

The check-list might be improved considerably by incorporation of a ranking or weighing scheme. A simple system might be to rate each idea under each consideration as to whether it is an idea which may be used today or in the long-range future. Other ranking methods might use a numerical or alphabetical scale to measure each quantity. It becomes extremely difficult to determine a fair and consistent scale to use. Not only must each item be ranked on the scale but these ratings must be compared with each other. The story has been told of an engineer who tried to use one of these scales to determine which of two girls he should marry. He finally determined that, even though one of the girls had the numerical advantage according to one of the evaluation scales, he did not really love her. It appears, therefore, that in any given situation one item or combinations of items may be of overwhelming importance.

Other schemes may assist the designer in selecting a method. He might attempt to select the best portion of each idea but may find that with each selection he has also included the worst of each idea. This happens when a compound of solutions is tried. The committee method for solving problems works in much this way. In addition it suffers from difficulties in communication and the inclusion of too many viewpoints. It has often been said that a camel looks as though it had been put together by such a committee.

We easily believe that which we wish. Corneille.

Another method is merely to delay a solution until a later date. This is based upon the theory that oftentimes the problem will solve itself. While this method has some merit under certain situations, its advantages have been highly overrated.

Probably the best recommendation is to attempt any one of these systems. By starting at any point and attempting some sort of classification, an understanding of the problem will evolve. As the designer attempts to list the advantages or to rate each idea or to use a check-list, his viewpoint will change and his enthusiasm for the task will mount. It is difficult to begin but begin you must. Once your feet are wet, your understanding of the task will grow.

HUMAN ELEMENT IN EVALUATION

THE HUMAN PROBLEMS involved in evaluation are well illustrated by the study of the following letter. It is a copy of a committee report concerning the invention of the telephone, dated April 1877. While not fully authenticated it more than likely occurred.

> Subject: Report of Special Technical Committee to consider the TELEPHONE as an investment.

1. The TELEPHONE is so named by its inventor, Mr. A. G. Bell, who sees for it a vast future as a means of personal communication by voice. He believes that one day they will be installed in every residence and place of business.
2. We note that Mr. Bell's profession is that of a voice teacher, and particularly a teacher of the deaf. He appears to have no direct experience with the telephone or any other form of communication, electrical or otherwise. Yet he claims to have discovered an instrument of great practical value in communication, which has been overlooked by the thousands of workers who have spent years in this field.
3. Mr. Bell's proposal to place his instruments in almost every home and business house (and this is the only way in which their potential may be realized) is fantastic in view of the capital costs of installing the endless numbers of wires and cables that would be demanded. The central exchanges alone would represent a huge outlay in real estate and buildings, to say nothing of the electrical equipment.
4. Mr. Bell expects that the public will use his instruments without the aid of trained operators. Any telegraph engineer will at once see the fallacy in this plan. The public simply cannot be trusted to handle

technical communications equipment. In any home where there are children, to mention only one point, there would inevitably be a high rate of breakage and frivolous use of the instruments. Furthermore, when making a call the subscriber must give the desired number verbally to the operator. No one on this Committee would like to be that operator, and have to deal with persons who may be illiterate, speak with lisps or stammers or foreign accents, or who may be sleepy or intoxicated when making a call.

5. While every telegram constitutes in itself a written record of what has been communicated, Mr. Bell's instrument uses nothing but the voice, which cannot be captured in any concrete form, and therefore there would be no record of what was said or agreed upon. We leave it to you to judge whether any sensible man of business would transact his affairs by such a means of communication.
6. Mr. Bell expects that the subscribers to this service will pay to have the instruments installed in their premises and will thereafter pay for each call made, with a monthly minimum even if no calls are made. We feel it very unlikely that any substantial number of people will agree to such an arrangement, in view of the telegraph offices which are now giving efficient round-the-clock service in every neighborhood and in the smallest towns, which charge only for actual messages sent according to length.
7. In conclusion, this Committee feels it must advise against any investment whatever in Mr. Bell's scheme. We do not doubt that it will find a few uses in special circumstances, such as between the bridge of a ship and the engine rooms, but any development of the kind and scale which Mr. Bell so fondly imagines is utterly out of the question.

(*Reprinted with permission from* Product Engineering)

In this letter the reader will note all of the stumbling blocks in our selection of a solution. Not only do others react to our ideas in this manner but we also do it to ourselves. Each of us has a fear of the unknown and a desire for security and therefore we resist any changes. Furthermore, if we should accept a new solution to an old problem, we would be admitting that we were wrong in the past. Since our behavior is the result of attitudes we hold, we resist any changes and find "logical" excuses for doing so. We must be extremely careful in our evaluation to question our habits, what we see, and how we think things should be done. We must come up with worthwhile answers, assume the innocence of children, taking nothing as obvious.

Most of us are defensive about our ideas. We tend to be easily pleased with our first efforts and assume a tremendous pride of ownership. It has been found from a study of management decisions that if an individual finds that his first solution is a satisfactory one, he is not likely to look for an alternative. The necessity for writing specifications prior to synthesis should be apparent as a means of preventing us from rationalizing our solution. Unless these specifications are written originally, the designer is tempted to determine the specifications from the solution.

Evaluation is always a threat, always creates a need for defensiveness, always means that some portion of experience must be denied to awareness. Carl Rogers.

The solution we select must be consistent with the time, materials, skills, etc., available for the solution. Sometimes we are easily pleased with our first solution. At other times we are faced with the problem of wanting to continue the solution to its ultimate refinements. We must be careful that our design is consistent with all the factors involved.

CREATIVE EVALUATION

THERE IS A REAL need for creative thinking at this point. In order to select a given solution wisely, a designer must anticipate even very remote difficulties which could be encountered. For honest evaluation he must determine the possible satisfactions at the present time and in time to come. He must try to anticipate the changing needs and desires of people and must actively get away from the present.

If he is to succeed in this ambitious task, he must be very willing to take calculated risks and to chance being wrong. He must have a stubborn persistence to complete the task. He must have a strong power of concentration, particularly in this age of telephones and other distractions. To be able to select that solution which he feels to be the best despite the opinions and attitudes of others, he must be honest with himself, and to a very marked degree, he must possess the ability of discernment and selectivity. *He must possess his own internal set of values which are only remotely influenced by the attitudes of others.*

SUMMARY

The goal in this phase of design is to weigh the various solutions and to make a decision or selection. The solutions should be compared with the original problem definitions and specifications and with any other criteria which may influence the final use and acceptance of the solution.

Many methods may be used to perform this evaluation. Some system is desirable since it decreases the possibility of forgetting to consider some aspect of the problem. A further merit of a system is that it permits us to get started and become motivated for the task. Classifying and comparing of the various aspects of the solution will help us to develop an understanding of the ideas and to winnow those of lesser value.

A child from the time he goes to school is taught it is very dangerous to fail. The inventor fails 9,999 times and if he succeeds once, he is in. Kettering.

The difficulties encountered in performing this evaluation and selection are largely human in nature. They result from our relationships with other people and our having to justify our selected solution. To some degree all of us have a resistance to change because we fear the problems which the solution may bring.

It is important to understand the part the various blocks play in our ability to creatively evaluate these ideas. It is necessary that we understand thoroughly all those factors which may prevent our seeing each idea in its most favorable light.

A sample work sheet to use as a guide . . .

Design Work Sheet

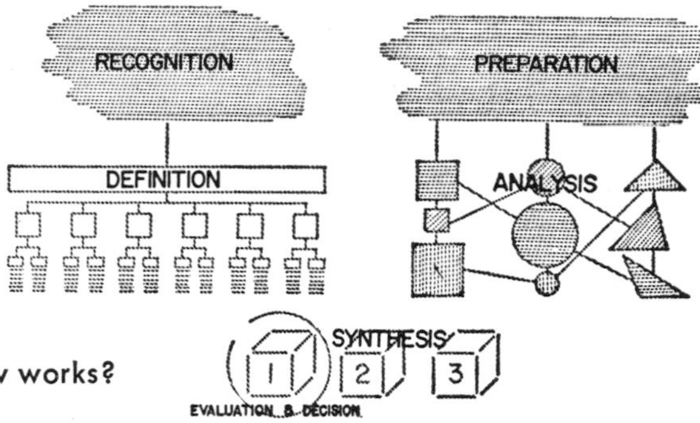

EVALUATION

Will the solution do the job?
What can I compare the solution to which I know works?
What checks can I make on the analysis?
Does it meet the specifications? (see definition)
Will it work in actual practice?
Is it acceptable to people, compatible with human nature?
Is it a balanced design?
Is it simple? Is it the simplest way of solving the problem?

Is each part really necessary?
What does each item contribute to the solution?
Is the solution timely?
What is the worth of the solution?
What ideas and opportunities have been overlooked?
What is likely to be the solution ten years from now?
Does the solution create any new problems?
What are the advantages and disadvantages of the solution regarding the following?

	Advantages	**Disadvantages**
Cost — development		
finished product		
operation		
Time — development		
production		
operation		
Accuracy of parts		
Power requirements		
Space requirements		
Tools required		
Materials required		
Skills required		
for manufacturing		
for operation		
Appearance		
Maintenance		
skill required		
safety		
cost		
Versatility		
Reliability		
due to wear		
due to breakage		
due to deflection		
Etc.		

8.

Presentation

THE FINAL PHASE in problem solving and design is the selling or presentation of the solution. The goal of this step is the eventual adoption of the conclusions of the engineer. Before others can be convinced of the validity and wisdom of the solution, the designer must be sure that the solution will accomplish the task and that it will work.

This phase is perhaps the most difficult of all and requires a high degree of creative ability. It is difficult because it involves other human beings with differences in habits, ideas and opinions. In addition, the analytical ability and training of the engineer may be a serious stumbling block in the way of putting his ideas into effect. Few fields of endeavor are concerned with analyzing problems to the degree engineering is. It is difficult for other people to appreciate fully the designer's specialized approach to the problem.

The engineer usually has little interest in the principles involved in sales. He feels it is sufficient that he understand the problem and that others automatically accept his wisdom and his conclusions. History affords countless illustrations of the failure of a solution because of the inability to sell the idea. John Ericsson became most famous as a designer and builder of the ironclad Monitor. He also became famous for designing a hot-air engine and the first steam fire engine using an artificial draft boiler. It was a frigid night on the first trial of the fire engine in London, but the engine successfully pumped water for five hours without a hitch while hand engines quickly froze and became useless. Furthermore, a brewery burned to the ground and Ericsson's engine was borrowed and kept at work day and night for months pumping beer from one vat to another. Unfortunately, London firemen and manufacturers of the old hand pump were against the new device. "You have to keep up steam. It's too powerful. Too heavy. It requires more water than London can provide." Eventually Ericsson withdrew in disgust and London was forced to live with its fire menace.

Why did these people object to the new solution? The way they acted was the result of the way they felt, of the way they saw things, and the way they thought things should be done. In other words, habits became the true stumbling block. A number of psychologists have remarked that the mind is an emergency organ. By habit we tend to solve problems and react to situations. Only when these habitual reactions fail, do we even try to use our mind to solve the problem. Even when we fail we very often continue to try old habits even though they have proved unsuccessful.

These habits produce a comfortable cushion and a feeling of security. We therefore fear any changes in these habits; we are not quite sure what an unknown solution will bring in terms of new problems. We fear to be ridiculed by others if we wrongly accept a new idea and we resent the criticism of other individuals. We don't want others to tip the boat. We would rather have the present solutions with all their shortcomings than chance the unknown future.

The way we feel about things results, then, in one or more of the following reactions to new solutions:

> We tried that before. That's not my job. We're all too busy to do that. It's too radical a change. Men will never buy it. We've never done that before. That's too ivory tower. Let's get back to reality. Why change it, it's still working ok. I don't like the idea. You're two years ahead of your time. You can't teach an old dog new tricks. Good talk but it would be impractical.
>
> We'll be the laughing stock. Top management will never go for it. Where did you dig that one up? We did all right without it. Maybe that will work in your

department, but not in mine. I know a fellow who tried it. We've always done it this way.

Each of these statements tend to crush acceptance of an idea. "What good is it?" is supposed to be psychologically overwhelming. More often than not, the so-called professional opinions are based on emotion rather than experience. Quite often the other person gives the designer feigned praise and in doing so he is saying, "Now, I have done my part since I have admitted the obvious in a cautious sort of way. But I don't see any reason to open the bulkhead of my compartmentalized, domain-oriented thinking. My mental living room is completely furnished; I don't need to buy anything new—it is comfortable just as it is." Comments like "It's obvious" or "Oh, it's just an idea, I have thousands of them" actually are intended to convey to the imposter such blinding brilliance that he wouldn't dare to admire his own minor effort.

Other examples of the failure of a solution are legion. One company could not sell a new electronically-controlled internal grinder in place of an old cam-controlled model and was informed by the sales department: "People preferred the cam model because it was familiar." Textile loom manufacturers continued to sell old models because, "People didn't want to complicate the operations and maintenance with new-fangled gadgets." When the companies first attempted to sell automatic controls to chemical plants, the reaction was, "Where can we find half a man for an operator?" While American products in general are considered in foreign countries as superior to Russian designs, in some fields people in India often tend to be more interested in the crude machine from Communist China than our latest American product. This is for a very human reason: it is far closer to what they understand and what they think they too can learn to manufacture, than is our finished American machine.

Problems of adoption are, in general, human problems. The people to whom the solution must be sold are management, the craftsman, the seller, the operator, the individuals who benefit. Perhaps their fears and habits appear in different areas, but they are motivated and react much as we do. The solution of these human problems becomes the key to adoption. These human problems can be approached and solved as any other problem of design.

PRESENTATION SUGGESTIONS

REMEMBER THAT salesmaster—the medicine man? He was an expert in the art of pre-selling. He conditioned his audience by proposing a bit at a time, leaving a period for acceptance before the next stage. He started with the known areas and proceeded to the unknown. As he did so, the whole idea, springing forth completely grown, was spared the contempt of his audience. The people had grown with the idea, had contributed to it, or moderated it constructively. They had participated in the solution. Each of us feels that if the other individual does the thing it must be wrong. However, if we ourselves do it, the idea must be ok. We like to gradually approach an idea through a prelude, absorb its development, and go on to a climax or recommendation. In that way we may, step by step, change the way we think, how we see things, and how we think they should be done.

Pasteur had quite a difficult time selling his concept of bacteria over the opposition, which favored the theory of spontaneous generation. However, he managed to sell his idea at a lecture in Paris in 1864 by holding up one of his flasks containing an infusion of hay and saying, "And I wait, I watch, I question it, begging it [spontaneous generation] to recommence for me the beautiful spectacle of the first creation . . . but it is dumb, because I have kept it from the only thing man cannot produce, the germs which float in the air, from life, and life is a germ and a germ is life." Pasteur knew how to put it across. His audience had grown with the idea.

The problem becomes one of how to accomplish this goal. A little boy asked his mother for some money with which to purchase a new toy and she refused. He then approached his father with the same request. Did he get the money and the toy? Of course he did. And to do so he did not need a course in "How to win friends and influence people." He used his common sense, his inherent abilities. All each of us needs to do is to place ourselves in the position of the person to whom the idea must be sold.

If we so project ourselves, we may ask: What do I want to know? How do I know it's right? What will result from the idea? What will be good, or bad?

What are the advantages and disadvantages? What other solutions are possible? The people to whom it must be sold have not been as intimately in contact with the problem as has the solver. Others may not be acquainted with the ideas and the reasons why other solutions will not work. It is necessary to show them that of all possible ideas, including their own, this is the best solution.

"The only thing that keeps me from acting on your plans, Hendricks, is fear . . . Fear of losing my shirt!!"

Other people respond favorably to well-organized information, much as we ourselves do. They are impressed also by an efficient presentation. A neat, orderly report conveys a feeling of confidence just as does an orderly and efficient doctor's office. Treatment may be no better, but the confidence is there. All assumptions should be clearly stated, all justifications for formulas, all sources of information and facts. A report should be presented in such a way as to attract attention and to stimulate curiosity.

Basically we must in a very simple manner go through the entire solution of the problem. Usually we begin with a conclusion and recommendation since they are the goals of the problem. However, we should also answer such questions as: What was the problem? What did I know, and what did I assume? How did I analyze the data? What were some of the possible solutions including those which were rejected? What solution was selected and why was it used? What checks or tests were made to determine its feasibility? What recommendations, generalizations are possible? How would I interpret and evaluate the solution selected?

It is wise to start with the known and habitual and proceed into unknown territory. In doing this, the work should be so arranged as to give the reader complete confidence in what has been done. It should be presented so well that others regard it as simple and wonder why they hadn't thought of it. It should be complete, subject to quick checking, and written in such a manner that anyone could return to the work at a later date and quickly understand the problem. It should convey a feeling of sincerity and it should possess the somewhat conflicting qualities of clarity, comprehension, and brevity.

Fluency . . .

"Boss, I've been thinking . . ."

Information can only be received through the senses. We must make deliberate effort to convey ideas effectively and efficiently to them. Vision is the principal receptor of information, followed by hearing, feel, smell and taste. Difficulties in reception and understanding are encountered in effective communication. Researchers have found that only about 70 per cent of the spoken word is actually received and understood (and then not necessarily understood as was intended). Therefore, complete understanding comes through the repetition and redundancy present in speech. If additional distractions and background noises are present, reliability of reception is even less. In receiving information we must often convert from one set of symbols, say an orthographic drawing, to the symbols we most readily understand, such as three-dimensional objects. In view of these handicaps, every effort should be made to increase the efficiency of transmission of accurate information, and to understand the problems which are involved.

A study of disciplines other than engineering will help the engineer to overcome communication difficulties. Understanding the problems a lawyer encounters in conveying ideas between individuals—in contract negotiations and courts of law—and observing the lawyer's solutions, will aid the designer.

The Human Use of Human Beings, by Norbert Wiener, should provide a better understanding of how information is received and what is done with it. In any organization, problems such as the deliberate falsification of data, personnel's seeing only favorable facts (selective perception), and the uncertainty involved in absorption of such information, present real challenges.

In addition to receiving and absorbing information pertaining to the solution, it is necessary for the receiver to interpret it. Inherently, each of us is somewhat lazy or at least conserves his energies. The presentation should be made so that the people to whom the idea must be sold may interpret this solution with the least expenditure of energy.

It must be remembered also that each of us harbors certain preconceived ideas, has certain axes to grind, and a certain world to protect. When a group of middle-management executives were presented with a given problem situation and each asked what problem the new president should first deal with, 83 per cent of sales personnel thought of a sales problem, while only 29 per cent of the other managers saw the fundamental problem as a sales one. In a given situation, each person will react to the problem differently and will see it in a different light.

". . . 'not only that,' I went on defiantly, I'll stake my job on it: this design is without flaw!"

The acceptance of the idea will also be influenced by the momentary objectives of the organization. These objectives are, in general, poorly defined, ambiguous, and varying from time to time. The acceptability of a given idea will vary depending upon a present condition—say fire, theft, budget, recession, or competition—and its relation to company objectives. It would be difficult, for example, to get acceptance on a design involving a large expenditure of money at a time when there is a general economy drive within the organization.

From the preceding discussion it should be apparent that the designer should expect changes in his solution due to variations of opinion and background. It is necessary to play a psychological give-and-take in order to get the design across. We need not, however, apologize for a given decision or opinion which is at variance with the group.

TECHNIQUES OF PRESENTATION

THE USE OF SKETCHES, graphs, drawings, and photos, together with written explanation, should be encouraged. These visual aids can often convey information more effectively and efficiently than pages of words. Freehand but neat sketches are effective; the architect's use of renderings and sketches has much to recommend it; models become very effective. As in the case of the medicine man, something should be used to challenge the curiosity of the receiver. An architect once presented his solution on a window shade to catch the attention of the client. Some songwriters once sold their song by writing it on a large piece of plywood and mailing it to a singer, postcard fashion. The winner of a large number of slogan contests was once asked the secret of his success. He replied that half the task was deliberately thinking up a large number of solutions and selecting from them the best one. The other half of the task was to think of some clever and unusual way of presenting his solution so as to catch the attention of the contest managers. However, in attempting to present the idea cleverly and catch the attention, we need not stoop to the cheap and sensational. The presentation should be professional, and genuinely sincere.

As we have attempted in other phases of problem solving to reduce the material to a brief and systematic form, sample work sheets have been included for this phase of the work also. If the designer will deliberately and systematically try to solve this human problem in

"Hello, Ed? Bill. I was just wondering — is this a rough draft you sent down or were you just cleaning your pen?"

Design News

the same way he tried to solve the original physical engineering problem, he will go a long way toward gaining acceptance of his solution.

SUMMARY

People must be sold on the solution which we have selected in order that it be efficiently and effectively put into practice. An idea or problem solution, is of little value until it is sold to someone. Professor John E. Arnold of Stanford University writes, "I am very disturbed and upset by the great numbers of people who are writing and speaking today on this general subject, and who seem to believe that the idea is, in itself, the beginning and end of the creative process. Ideas can frequently be a dime a dozen. It is only when ideas are transferred into workable prototypes that I believe they have value."

The individuals to whom the solution must be sold are present at all levels of the organization and are much the same as ourselves. They are not machines, but human beings possessing fears, opinions, and habits that must be changed before the solution is to be adopted. These habits can be changed and the fears erased if the individual is brought to understand the problem and how it was solved. It is important that he participates in its solution and grows with it.

Also see "The Creative Engineer," in *Creative Engineering,* ASME.

There is a definite *need at this phase of the work to get off the beaten path. Just as it is necessary to use creative ideas to arrive at a solution, every possible and unusual idea must be used to win over all those concerned with the problem we have solved.*

It is easy to see why so many good ideas never get used. After the solution has been found, the psychological lift and excitement may have diminished. The solver must be a strongly determined person in order to see the problem through the often routine and sometimes discouraging final phases. It should be emphasized that sometimes these final phases require a tremendous exercise of creative ability. Many worthwhile ideas have been lost in these last steps.

A sample work sheet to use as a guide . . .

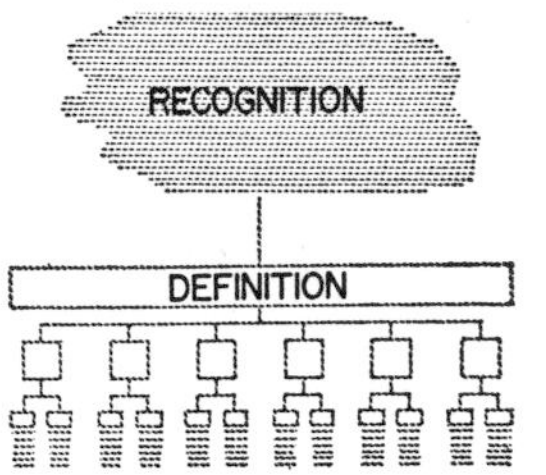

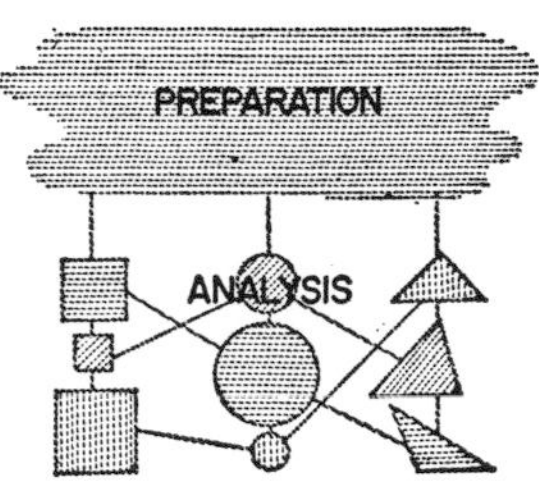

Design Work Sheet

PRESENTATION—SELLING AN IDEA

I WANT HIM TO—
(In answer to, "Just what do you want me to do?")

ADVANTAGES OF DOING WHAT YOU ASK (In answer to, "What's in it for me?")	HOW TO GET THIS ADVANTAGE ACROSS TO HIM
1.	1. A. B. C.
2.	2. A. B. C.
3.	3. A. B. C.
4.	4. A. B. C.
5.	5. A. B. C.

FINAL PLAN OF ACTION REGARDING DESIGN

What to Do	Who	When	Where	How
Step 1.				
2.				
3.				
4.				
5.				

9.

Design Creativity-A Conclusion

A WIDELY HELD ASSUMPTION among engineers is that the most important factors in solving problems are intelligence and an accumulation of factual knowledge. Holding this assumption, it becomes difficult to explain and understand the difference in output of two engineers possessing apparently equal knowledge and apparently equal intelligence. Each of us has observed situations involving two such individuals, one of whom produces only routine run-of-the-mill answers while the other is capable of the unusual and unique. It has been stated that there exists such a lack of creative individuals that it is possible to find only one or two per million of population. We are interested in knowing why such a difference exists in the quality of output. Or more practically, we individually are interested in knowing how we might design and come up with the unusual, the clever, and the progressive idea. We are interested in specifically knowing how we might improve our creative abilities.

It is important that we agree on a definition of creativity. As used thus far in the discussion of problem solving, creative ability represents the ability to solve problems in a manner which is new to the problem solver himself. It is not really important to our understanding of creative ability and its development whether or not a particular combination of ideas has been previously discovered by other individuals. Nor does it really matter in the process of coming up with unusual ideas, whether or not the scheme eventually turns out to be practical. Creativity represents the ability to get out of a mental rut and the ability to look at things in new and different ways.

The intellectual ability of an individual is important, particularly in the complex and abstract situations encountered by the engineer.

Intelligence has never been uniquely or satisfactorily defined. Intelligence, as measured by an intelligence test, appears to be the ability to analyze a problem and to break apart the bits of information. Since analysis is a part of creative problem solving we rightly find that creativity correlates positively with intelligence and is far stronger in that correlation than in its correlation with any other ability, such as mechanical aptitude.

But in order to solve problems and to do so in an unusual manner, other factors are also significant. We may classify intelligence and talent as inherent or inherited abilities. They represent the potential with which we start life. Knowledge is another significant factor and represents our accumulated experience not only from former education but every life situation. But in addition to the foregoing, our problem solving ability is also affected by our attitude, drive, and by the methods we employ. These represent our reaction to our environment.

If we are trying to understand the why of the differences which exist between a creative and a non-creative engineer we do not have an easy task. We are not quite sure why a given individual responds to his environment by becoming creative. How a man thinks depends upon the kind of person he is, the experiences he has undergone in life, and the value he places on things. But if we want to know what we are doing wrong when we attempt to solve problems and end up with the routine, and what we should do differently to avoid this, then some help is possible. In the pages that follow we shall (1) try to understand why individuals are not creative, (2) what personal qualities are found helpful, and (3) what to do to accomplish more creative ideas. Much already has been said concerning creativity in prior discussions. The purpose of the following will be to collect and expand these ideas.

"Our artisans are as good as theirs! Why don't we have the wheel?"

WHY DESIGNS ARE NOT CREATIVE

Genius, in truth, means little more than the faculty of perceiving in an unhabitual way. William James.

IT HAS BEEN shown that the fundamental reason for our not coming up with unusual solutions and unusual methods when we are designing is habit—we think in familiar terms; we try to solve new problems on the basis of our experience and methods used in the past. Our habits transfer from one situation to another and we try to use them when they do not even apply. These habits are reinforced by our perception, by our culture, and by our emotions. They represent blocks to our thinking.

If you are not convinced that we solve problems by habit, try to consciously tie your necktie or to explain to another individual how you do it. Momentarily put on your wife's blouse if you can and see if you can conveniently button the buttons. If you were asked to consciously drive a car from one town to another, could you consciously perform all the operations? If you have the physical dexterity to ride a bicycle are you conscious of how you really perform this task?

When we try to solve a new problem we can use only our own knowledge and that of others. However, our accumulated knowledge may fail us because we do not use it creatively, that is, we do not free it from our usual habit patterns. When this happens, we must deliberately *work* to rearrange our knowledge to find a new solution. Of course, if we are successful in solving the problem, we try to generalize this solution and we have acquired *new* habits!

The habitual solving of problems is both good and bad. On the credit side, habit saves our mind for the more useful and more routine tasks of life. Furthermore, it saves our sanity, for if we had to deliberately solve every problem, life would become intolerable. In

terms of disadvantages, habit causes us to try old methods even if they are unsuccessful—as the chicken does when she continues to try to go through the fence rather than go around the end. These habits hamper our ability to find other methods for solving the problem.

See *Journal of Experimental Psychology,* **44**: 288-91, 1952.

Duncker worked out an interesting experiment which illustrates how habits cause faults in our thinking. The first task presented to some students was the mounting of 3 candles vertically on a screen. Among the objects available were 3 pasteboard boxes, matches, and thumbtacks. The solution was to mount one candle on each box by melting wax on the box, sticking the candle to it and then tacking the boxes to the screen. The second problem involved suspension of three cords from a board attached to an overhead beam. Among the objects available were two screw hooks and a gimlet (a device for boring holes), the objects from which the cords may be hung. The third problem consisted of attaching four small black squares to a large white one and then hanging the large square from an eyelet in a beam. Among the objects available were paper clips which could be used to attach the small squares to the large one, and one of them when bent into a hook would serve to hang the large square from the eyelet. All the subjects were given the problems in the same order. For one group the solutions were burdened with prior uses of the objects. The candles, matches, and tacks for the box problem were presented in the boxes. The gimlet was used to start the holes for the screw hooks. The four black squares were attached to the white one with a paper clip. For the control group, no preutilization was used. Only 41 per cent of the "burdened" group solved the problems, while 86 per cent of the group involving no pre-utilization of the objects did so. In addition, significant differences in the average time required to solve the problems occurred for the two groups, almost twice as much time being taken by the "burdened" group. This illustration points out that the pre-utilization of objects (the use of the box as a container, the use of the gimlet to start holes, and the use of the paper clips to hold papers together) resulted in mental blocks in solving the problem. This type of block is often called functional fixedness.

The Maier two-cord problem, previously discussed, illustrated that specific prior experience limited the perception of an object's properties and made all the solver's experiences less available as problem solving tools. Because of habit we often continue to use the methods in solving problems which are not necessarily appropriate to the situations. This is called mechanization or rigidity.

Also H. G. Birch, *Journal of Experimental Psychology,* **41:** 121-25, 1951.

This rigidity is best illustrated by the Duncker water-jar problem. For this task the subject is told that he should measure out a certain number of units of water using given sizes of containers. For example, given a large tank of water, a three-unit jar and a five-unit jar, measure out two units. The solution is: fill the five-unit jar from a tank, fill the three-unit container from the five-unit jar leaving two units in the five-unit jar. The solution may be written as $5-3=2$ or $A-B$ equals required amount of water. The solution to the first problem below is $B-A-2C=$ required amount. The reader is asked to solve the following problems and formulate a general solution before proceeding to the discussion.

Also R. E. Adamson, D. W. Taylor, *Journal of Experimental Psychology,* **47:** 122-26.

Problem		Given the following empty jars as measures			Obtain the required amount of water
No.	Kind	A	B	C	
1.	Sample	29 units	3 units	units	20 units
2.	Set producing	21	127	3	100
3.	Set producing	14	163	25	99
4.	Set producing	18	43	10	5
5.	Set producing	9	42	6	21
6.	Set producing	20	59	4	31
7.	Crucial 1	23	49	3	20
8.	Crucial 2	15	39	3	18
9.	Extinction	28	76	3	25
10.	Crucial 3	18	48	4	22
11.	Crucial 4	14	36	8	6

In the foregoing experiment, problems 1 through 6 were solvable by the method of $B—A—2C$. These similar problems serve to produce a set and mechanization. Problems 7 through 11 test for the presence of the set and are solvable by this method and also by a shorter method using only two jars, *A* and *C*. Problem 9 is solvable only by method $A—C$; problems 10 and 11 can be solved by either method. Without any admonition such as "don't be blind," over 35 per cent of the individuals will solve problems 7 and 8 by the longer method. For problem 9, solvable by only one method, 50 to 90 per cent of the individuals fail to solve the problem within 2½ minutes. This rigidity is very widespread and it appears in persons of widely varying ages, educational and ability levels. Some individuals showed no set effect.

Another experiment illustrating functional fixedness is one involving the use of water to remove a ping-pong ball from a rusty upright pipe. In general, people will see the solution which involves using dirty water but they are not apt to see the use of clear, cold drinking water to perform the same task. The block to creative problem solving is our own antiquated thinking. The blind application of old habits to new situations results in an alarming increase in the number of roadblocks between the concept and the completion of a problem.

Fault in Methods

Often the failure to solve a problem creatively results from the failure of the habits themselves. Sometimes the methods we employ are not generalized enough to be applicable to a range of problems. On the other hand, the methods may not be specific or adaptable enough to take into consideration the variations which occur from problem to problem. Often

failure results from inability to specifically define what the problem is. Sometimes we fail to gather sufficient information or include extraneous data. Often we fail to find relationships among the various facts or often too few possible solutions. We may fail to recognize the problem or we may fail to recognize all factors, thinking that some things are obvious and trivial. We may fail to associate cause and effect or just forget to do one phase of the work.

We distinctly need a *system* so that we may maximize the possibility of solutions by minimizing the things we may forget. Such a system must be flexible enough to meet each situation, and must be simple enough to become somewhat habitual. Too often it has been assumed that designers instinctively acquire this ability to approach problems. On the contrary, designers usually require specific training and experience in setting up problems and solving them. Since each problem involves a peculiar combination of circumstances, it is impossible to solve each by merely finding an example in some book and copying the solution. Nor will a designer develop a very thorough and complete system of his own by being presented a series of examples and then being expected to find the common denominators of the solutions. In solving a design problem we should use *all* the possible tools we possess, much as we would play on *all* the keys of a musical instrument. A purchasing agent who would limit himself to one source of supply would be thought very incapable. Certainly, we as engineers are open to criticism if we use only one method of solution or focus our attention on only one phase of the design. A check-list of problem solving has been included in the Appendix to serve as a guide in evaluating individual methods of solution.

Breakdown in Habits—Blocks

Often the failure to come up with unusual solutions lies within the person himself. "Do you have a solution or are you part of the problem?" is a question which illustrates a need for understanding our relationship to problem solution. When more than one person works on a problem, the difficulties are compounded by a multiplicity of viewpoints, personalities, and mental blocks. "A committee never had an idea. An idea is inherently a one-man invention." is perhaps a severe criticism of the group approach but it illustrates the difficulties involved.

A number of psychological experiments show how various conditions may affect a solver's habits and modify his methods of solving the problems. Fifty volunteer students were asked to decode cryptographic sentences which were given to them. Some sentences were neutral, for example, "Most gardens are damp in spring." Some were threat provoking such as, "My family doesn't respect my judgment," or, "It is stupid to believe there is a God." More time was required to decode the threatening sentences than was required for the neutral ones. In addition, more personal threats were included before some of the neutral sentences such as, "Can't you do it a little faster?" or "You aren't concentrating, I'm afraid. You can do better than this." Considerably more errors were made for the threatening sentences than for those not preceded by threats. It appears that an individual's problem solving ability is affected both by his reactions to events and his reactions to others.

A. Combs and C. Taylor, *Journal Abnormal Social Psychology,* 47: 420-24, 1952.

In another experiment, some subjects were given tests and were told that they were participating in an evaluation program, the results of which would go on their records. It was emphasized that the test was an

R. S. Lazarus, and C. W. Eriksen, *Journal Experimental Psychology,* **43:** 100-05, excellent predictor of college success. They were urged to do well since this information would be used by the faculty to consider their status in school. The experimental group was told upon completion of the test that they had done poorly. They were reminded of the seriousness of the problem and were told that another test administration would give greater certainty to their true ability. At intervals during this retest experimenters called out false norms. The control group, on the other hand, was told they had all done well but, since it was important to be sure of each student's ability, another measure would be taken. Four interruptions were again made but the announced norms were well within the performances of the given subjects. The experimental group showed an increase in errors for the second test, while the control group showed a decrease. It was concluded from this that individuals vary greatly in their reactions to stress; that errors increased under stress but were somewhat compensated for by increase in speed; and that individuals with higher academic grades tended to be less affected by stress.

We may conclude from these and other experiments that stress and frustration cause an increase in the mental blocks which operate to prevent us from solving problems. Such stress and frustration are provided in problem situations by our environment and by other people. Our reaction to each of these will determine the degree of effectiveness of our designing.

In solving problems we are motivated by a number of factors, among them the pleasure of accomplishment and the desire for satisfactory relations with other people. If the designer is motivated toward creative answers and getting off the beaten path, he runs into conflict with peoples' habits. Other people, reacting to the creative designer's work, are fearful he will build some sort of Frankenstein monster. Creating *is* a fearsome thing. It requires us to destroy old ideas close to our hearts and give up opinions which have been with us for a long time. People fear the unknown and what they don't understand. Creative ideas are often associated with unemployment, dislocation, changes in our way of life, and an admission that perhaps we weren't doing things in the best way in "the good old days." This fear is clearly illustrated in the history of science by the notable lack of acceptance accorded to various discoveries and inventions.

In other words, the designer is asked to be creative but not too much. He must not upset the applecart and destroy the habits of people just when they have gotten around to living with them. Should he run contrary to the habitual way of thinking he takes a chance of being ostracized. This has become the high tide of mediocrity, the great era of the "goof off." It is no longer socially acceptable to subscribe to the principle of *hard work.*

See *The Organization Man,* by William H. Whyte.

In addition, creation requires the conquering of a very personal problem. The same problem of fear of the unknown is operative at a personal level. The creation of a new idea requires very hard and tedious work; it is not the result of accident. It requires us to labor without any assurance of success when we can think of a thousand other things we would rather do. We find ourselves stumbling over our own emotions and feelings and we find it much more comfortable to solve other peoples' problems rather than our own. Nor do we have any assurance that should we succeed, we would be rewarded. The usual solution to this unhappy state of affairs is a compromise. It is easier to continue to use our own and other people's old habits. We thereby decrease our chance of failing and at the same time we maximize our chances for finding only a routine answer. By relying too heavily upon our habit patterns to solve the problem itself and to solve the problems involved in our relationships with others we are likely to end up with one or more of the following barriers: (1) unwillingness to dream (2) superficial thinking (3) wishful thinking (4) resistance to change (5) easy distraction by others (6) desire to be logical (7) fear of ridicule (8) fear of making a mistake.

So it is apparent how the habitual use of old methods ties us down in engineering design. The way we see things and the way we think things should be done makes us continue to use methods long after improvements are available. Scientists currently are having difficulty in understanding the phenomena which lead to the theory of wave mechanics, because they have habitually thought in terms of particles. Another generation, freed of this habit, will be able to grasp the facts with less difficulty.

The following poem aptly illustrates the solution of a problem and shows how habit stands in the way of new and improved solutions:

THE CALF PATH

One day through the primeval wood
A calf walked home as good calves should;
But made a trail all bent askew,
A crooked trail as all calves do.

Since then three hundred years have fled,
And I infer the calf is dead.

But still he left behind his trail,
And thereby hangs my moral tale.
The trail was taken up next day
By a lone dog that passed that way;
And then a wise bellwether sheep
Pursued the trail o'er hill and glade
Through those old woods a path was made.

And many men wound in and out,
And dodged and turned and bent about
And uttered words of righteous wrath
Because 'twas such a crooked path;
But still they followed—do not laugh—
The first migrations of that calf,
And through this winding wood-way stalked
Because he wobbled when he walked.

This forest path became a lane
That bent and turned and turned again;
This crooked lane became a road,
Where many a poor horse with his load
Toiled on beneath the burning sun,
And traveled some three miles in one.
And thus a century and a half
They trod the footsteps of that calf.

The years passed on in swiftness fleet,
The road became a village street;
And thus, before men were aware,
A city's crowded thoroughfare.
And soon the central street was this
Of a renowned metropolis;
And men two centuries and a half
Trod in the footsteps of that calf.

Each day a hundred thousand rout
Followed this zigzag calf about
And o'er his crooked journey went
The traffic of a continent.

A hundred thousand men were led
By one calf near three centuries dead.
They followed still his crooked way,
And lost one hundred years a day;
For thus such reverence is lent
To well-established precedent.

Sam Walter Foss - 1895

Persistence . . .

"You're falling behind again, Ernie."

TRAITS OF THE CREATIVE ENGINEER

An essential trait of the creative designer is his drive, his initiative, and his persistence. In order to solve the problem he must get started and this is a difficult task.

Constructive Nonconformity . . .

"I like the way Albert uses his head!"

Self Confidence . . .

"I get the impression we're considered a necessary evil around here . . ."

H. G. Birch, *Journal Comparative Psychology,* **38:** 295-317, 1945.

Motivation

It is tempting to take a course much like that taken by a certain drunk. He was looking for his cuff links near a street light one night and was presently joined by a sober stranger. After much searching with no success the sober one inquired whether the drunk actually was sure he had lost the object in that location. "No," replied the drunk, "the light's just better here." Very often we act as he did and try to solve only the easy and convenient problems.

Motivations for solving problems can be many-fold. The story of Scheherazade illustrates the skill we may possess if we are properly motivated. This young lady from *A Thousand and One Nights* was told that her life would be spared so long as she was able to think up entertaining tales. The thousand and one nights testify to her success.

A recent study ranked the motivations of engineers as follows: desire to solve problems 68 per cent, personal gratification obtained by accomplishment 64 per cent, desire to win prestige 64 per cent, desire to advance in financial position 42 per cent, desire to advance in title 14 per cent. Whatever an individual's goals, he must use the above or other reasons for getting started on the design. These are helps for getting away from the mediocre. Some writers have maintained that a creative individual most possess, as the Apostle Paul did in the Bible, a "thorn in the flesh." At any rate, something must "make us tick" and we must search for this illusive quality.

Moderate motivation is best; too little leads to a worthless solution and too much reduces flexibility. This was illustrated by depriving some animals of food for various periods of time and then testing their ability to solve a given problem. The most time was taken by those chimpanzees which had been deprived of food for only two hours. The next longest time was taken by those deprived of food for 36 and 48 hours respectively. Low motivation (the chimps were rewarded food upon successful completion of the task) was shown in the animals' being easily diverted from the problems by various extraneous factors. Their behavior tended to deteriorate to a series of nondirected acts. Under conditions of very intense motivation (long periods of food deprivation) the animals concentrated on the task to the exclusion of the other factors in the situation which were nonessential to the solution of the problem. Also, the frequent occurrence of frustration responses (tantrums and screaming) when a stereotyped response proved inadequate, hindered the efforts of the intensely motivated. The animals who worked under intermediate conditions of motivational intensity showed behavior which was characterized by both direction and flexibility. The food acted as a determining factor in the direction of their organizing new patterns, but they still were capable of responding to other relevant features of the problem situation.

High Motivation . . .

"I've found the best way to make Smedley work hard is to let him think he's designing a machine to replace me."

Charles Steinmetz, quite a creative person himself, made the following statement, "If a young man goes about his work as a means of making a living only, I am not interested in him. However, I am interested if he seems to do his work for the work's sake, for the satisfaction he gets out of doing it. If I were able to bequeath one virtue to him I would give him the spirit of divine discontent, for without it the world would stand still. The man hard to satisfy moves forward. The man satisfied with what he has done moves backward."

See "Creativity and Culture," Morris Stein, *Journal of Psychology,* 36: p. 311, 1953.

Active Curiosity, Sensitivity to Problems

To begin solving problems a designer must recognize what problems exist. To do this, he must be sensitive to his environment. To him, the obvious must not be obvious. He must continually ask *why, how*. *Why* is the grass green? *Why* does a steam locomotive carry green or white flags? *How* can a locomotive go around a curve without slipping if both wheels are rigidly attached to the axle?

Sensitivity to Problems . . .

"And then when we idle it down she sounds like this—"

This sensitivity to problems is important since it helps the designer anticipate difficulties to be encountered with any proposed solution. If you were asked to give a list of improvements for an electric light bulb, I'm sure that you would be able to furnish quite an extensive list. These improvements are merely answers to problems that exist. Make them cooler. Make them so they don't break. Make them less expensive. Make them so they last longer. Make them easier to insert. The fact that an individual is able to find improvements is evidence of his sensitivity to problems. Many accept these problems and disadvantages as a necessary part of the solution. When someone else shows how simple an improved solution is, we say, "Oh, that was obvious."

A creative designer must, furthermore, be continually open to experience, and extremely observant. Galvani's froglegs and Flemming's culture dish are examples of situations in which problems were solved by seeing and wondering about common conditions other people passed up. A number of years ago a manufacturer attempted to ball-burnish a small batch of rivets. Unfortunately the steel balls which were tumbled with the rivets were almost the same size as the hole in the end of the rivet. A third of the rivets came out with the ball neatly jammed into the hole. In the true spirit of creative scientific inquiry, the plant superintendent remarked, "Well, if we ever want to put balls in the ends of rivets, we'll know how."

See "Toward a Theory of Creativity," Carl Rogers, ETC, XI: No. 4.

To show that it is important to keep an open mind, look at the following problem:

> Given an isosceles triangle of base ten inches and altitude five inches, the area becomes 25 sq. inches. What is the area of an isosceles triangle whose base is ten inches and whose equal sides are each five inches long?

The mind must be kept open to the possibility that no solution exists to the problem. This is true in the preceding problem and the answer is 0 sq. inches.

Ability to
Think in Images . . .

Men who have designed machines have always needed an open mind. But never in the entire history of civilization has an inquiring attitude been as necessary as it is now. Without it, man could never reach the stars. With it, he will conquer space—and in the process conquer many other problems.

Willing to Take a Chance

It is essential that any designer trying for an unknown solution must be willing to make mistakes and to gamble. By statistics alone, we know that the majority of the proposed solutions will be failures. It is by sheer volume of ideas that a solution evolves which is unusual. There is no clear-cut path to success and along the way we must gamble that our effort will be wasted and that we will have to admit that we are only human.

Ability to
Toy With Ideas . . .

"Still stuck for ideas, Frisbie?"

If we look carefully, we will find that other successful problem solvers made their share of mistakes. Henry Ford forgot to put a reverse gear in his first automobile. Thomas Edison put two million dollars into a device which didn't work. Babe Ruth's home run production was matched by an equally impressive amount of strike-outs. Abraham Lincoln successfully used defeat in achieving victory. His record is as follows: (1) lost job 1832 (2) defeated for legislature

1832 (3) failed in business 1833 (4) elected to legislature 1834 (5) sweetheart died 1835 (6) defeated for speaker 1838 (7) defeated for nomination for Congress 1843 (8) elected for Congress 1846 (9) lost renomination (10) rejected for land officer 1849 (11) defeated for Senate 1854 (12) defeated for nomination for vice-president 1856 (13) again defeated for Senate 1858 (14) elected president 1860.

Initiative . . .

"Kraft suggested to the boss that we needed more floor space!"

We must therefore be bold and daring in the ideas and methods we use. No idea should be too wild for consideration. Edison, no slouch in creative thinking, said he would use anything as a filament in his light bulb, even Limburger cheese.

By habit we give ourselves excuses for not trying ideas. We try to carry ideas over from one situation to another, not realizing that the conditions have changed and have affected the usability of the idea. We can always think of all the reasons why we cannot use an idea or cannot do a thing. We develop a negative approach. One writer told recently of discussing with his father his father's idea of using the vacuum in an engine intake manifold to operate a windshield wiper. (This was over thirty years ago, when wipers were still hand-operated.) He explained very carefully all the physical restrictions and the equations to prove that such a wiper could not be built. His father merely commented, "It seems to me that college has taught you mostly what can't be done!" Here is the danger to our problem solving—a negative approach.

Flexibility . . .

"I lost my T-square!"

In November 1837, a distinguished British physicist demonstrated mathematically with equations nobody could question, that it was impossible to build a steamship capable of a nonstop voyage across the Atlantic Ocean. Printed copies of his lecture proving this fact arrived in Manhattan on April 24, 1838, aboard the SS Sirius, first ship to cross the Atlantic entirely under steam.

In 1806, a young officer named Zebulon Pike discovered a famous mountain in Colorado which bears his name. As he was prepared to move on into New Mexico, the young officer took a last look at the magnificent mountain which had defeated him in his attempts to scale it. He expressed himself as follows: "Yonder peak will never be scaled by mortal man." For many years a motor road has gone to the top of the peak, and the heights that "will never be scaled by mortal man" are ascended each year by thousands.

The following statements are examples of undesirable negative approaches to problems: (1) Commodore Vanderbilt dismissed Westinghouse and his new air brakes for trains with the remark that he had no time to waste on fools. (2) The people who lent Robert Fulton money for his steamboat project stipulated that their names be withheld, for fear of ridicule were it known that they supported anything so foolhardy. (3) Men insisted that iron ships would not float, that they would damage more easily than wooden ships when grounding, that it would be difficult to preserve their iron bottoms from rust, and that the iron would deflect the compass. (4) Joshua Coppersmith was arrested in Boston for trying to sell stock in the telephone. "All well-informed people know that it is impossible to transmit human voice over a wire." (5) Thomas A. Edison wrote a book giving reasons why an airplane couldn't fly—one week later the Wright brothers flew. Edison also gave his opinion that talking pictures would never come into general use because the public would not support them. (6) Chauncey DePew confessed that he had warned his nephew not to invest five thousand dollars in Ford stock because nothing has come along

Powers of Concentration . . .

"Eggle may crack with this one. He's trying to design a non-slipping, non-locking fastener."

to beat the horse. (7) Henry Norton, then president of Stevens Institute of Technology, protested against trumpeting results of Edison's experiments with electric lighting as a wonderful success, when everyone acquainted with the subject recognized it as a conspicuous failure.

Intellectual Integrity . . .

"Let's design a machine that does absolutely nothing."

Making a mistake is difficult to justify, either to ourselves or to others. Therefore we try to do all we can to ensure that we make none, or that if we do, it is not discovered. But in creative designing, we must understand that if we are no longer willing to gamble on failing, an important tool, trial and error, is deprived us. As soon as a person becomes overly concerned with social acceptability, he no longer thinks up ideas which are unconventional and different.

Creative Nonconformity, Internal Locus of Evaluation

Knowledge of the Fundamentals . . .

"Hello, engineering department?"

The designer, to come up with an unusual idea, must be bold and unconventional, he must get away from habit, and where others are involved, he must be a nonconformist. If he is to follow his own thinking he must certainly possess an internal locus of evaluation. He must be able to tell himself, in all honesty, which ideas are good and which are bad, which are right and which are wrong. Once he has made such a decision he must persist in his beliefs despite the negative opinions of others.

Conformity in thinking means the blind uncritical acceptance of other's beliefs and choices in the absence of personal conviction based on evidence and logical grounds. A degree of social conformity is essential to our existence. We could hardly live through a day if there were not a high degree of conformity to the laws of the land, to business practices, and to rules of conduct in personal relations. But if we conform in our manner of solving problems and do so to avoid the tiring labors involved in a task we are in difficulty. And if, perhaps, we conform to avoid moral responsibility or because of the stress laid upon harmony and agreement between members of a group, difficulties are sure to arise because: (1) the group is not necessarily always right; (2) conformity causes group agreement to be overvalued; (3) it promotes a tendency to disclaim error in one's thinking when that thinking differs from the group consensus; (4) conformity induces inertia, inhibitions, inflexibility; (5) it invites participants to express group opinions rather than private opinion.

The type and degree of conformity which an individual shows in a situation depends upon the individual. All people conform but creative people tend to conform less. Each of us tends to conform more when his actions affect others than when they only affect himself. The degree of conformity increases when differences in status between individuals increase or when one person feels he is being rejected by others. An increase in participation in the problem itself reduces the degree of conformity exhibited.

Groups tend to discourage deviate opinions. They prefer to continue with things as they are. On the other hand the creative person is attempting to change the status quo. However slight the proposed changes may be, they are a source of uncertainty for the people who are affected. Therefore the groups resist this uncertainty. They prefer the security of things as they are and they are inclined to reject the divergent opinion. Those individuals who deviate from the group are punished in some manner. Those who conform are rewarded. The degree with which an individual conforms to a situation depends on the

Ability to Suspend Critical Judgment . . .

"If you ask me, what we need is a clean sheet of paper."

meaning of the situation to him, the need for acceptance by the group, and his expertness in the task.

Psychologists have found three types of conformity. They are: (1) Cognitive. This individual is looking for a solution, he needs information, and he accepts the opinion of the group as being the most likely answer. (2) Expedient. He believes he has the correct answer but goes along with the group on a wrong answer in spite of this. (3) Passively suggestible. He lacks confidence in himself and his opinions, and accepts the group's opinion; they must be right, he must be wrong.

An interesting experiment in conformity has been performed. Five people were seated at panels. Each knew others were participating in the same task also but they could not see or talk to them. Each person was asked to answer questions by throwing an appropriate switch on his panel. He saw lights on his panel which, he was told, indicated the votes of the other four members. The subjects believed these lights were a communication system between the booths. However, the lights were controlled by the experimenter. Each subject was confronted with an apparent unanimous group opinion contrary to his own. Questions were projected on a screen and the subjects were asked to select a correct answer from the choices given. Questions varied from simple perception tests (which line is the longest?) to factual-logical questions (vocabulary, completion of number series) to attitude and opinion questions. Each person was subjected to group pressures by manipulating the lights to show unanimous group agreement on the least likely answer. For example, he saw that line 1 was longest; the group is voting for line 2 which is clearly shorter.

How did the subjects vote? The groups showed interesting differences. Some people didn't conform at all while others conformed most of the time. Women conformed more than men, while the older individuals conformed less than the younger.

The passive conformer feels inferior under stress. He rationalizes his internal conflict by redefining ("They must want the shortest line, not the longest.") or by his own lack of skill ("My eyes are no good, I can't do this kind of a test.") The expedient conformer admits he went along with the group and after the test can go back and answer the questions correctly.

There are two types of nonconformists also. They are: (1) the individual who really thinks he is correct, and (2) the individual who always adopts an opposite viewpoint. It is the first type we would like to encourage; he has been called the constructive nonconformist. To achieve this constructive nonconformity a person must have a high degree of self-confidence. He must possess passion for accuracy and hatred for self-deception if he is to have the courage of conviction. He must set for himself exacting standards so that he may select a solution and be convinced of its propriety. He must be determined and courageous since he is likely to be a minority. He must know that the majority is not always right and must stick by his opinion in the face of theirs.

Since he is less defensively conformist and feels less need of being forced into a standard pattern, he may permit himself to be more responsive to his emotions. We have discovered previously that the subconscious mind plays a large part in creatively solving problems. The constructive nonconformist always finds less need for resorting to logic and feels freer to use such subjective tools as hunches and intuition.

The man with unusual ideas has choices to make in relationships with others. He can give up, in effect admitting defeat and choosing a humdrum life; or, persist in the job and risk the chance of becoming "a character." If he chooses the unqualified latter course, he may find himself more and more a social outcast with others who are unsympathetic to his problems. But happily, he can choose a wise middle ground. He can persist in his ideas but do so in full recognition of their effect on other people. And he can understand *why* other people react the way they do and be sympathetic. In time, his experience, knowledge, and skill with others will grow, and his effectiveness will be greatly increased.

Research is an organized method for keeping you reasonably dissatisfied with what you have. Kettering.

Miscellaneous Abilities

Certainly, there are other extremely useful abilities which assist in the creative solution of problems. No problem can be solved without raw material and data. Therefore the designer must possess an extensive knowledge of fundamentals. It does little good for the engineer to memorize equations and other facts. To solve new problems he must understand the relationships which exist *between* facts and *between* various fields of interest. Numerical values and equations should not interfere with the constructive functioning of the mind. These may be looked up and determined as required. But having to look up basic principles and concepts of engineering for each problem would, of course, mar the efficiency of the solver.

Simultaneous Consideration of Several Ideas . . .

"Off button? . . . Off button!— I knew I'd forgotten something!"

He must, furthermore, possess certain abilities, some of which may, we can hope, be the incidental byproducts of engineering education. He must be able to consider simultaneously several ideas and be able to suspend judgment until the problem and facts are understood. He must be able to tolerate ambiguity and be able to sit down beside a problem whose methods of solution are as yet unknown to him. He must be able to toy with ideas; be able to manipulate them into various combinations and configurations. In general, the creative engineer prefers the more complex situations and enjoys thinking in images and in analogies. These qualities may be combined under the general title, fluency of ideas.

Willingness to take Calculated Risks . . .

CREATIVE TECHNIQUES

In trying to find the magic tool which will insure clever and creative answers we have discovered that our failures in problem solving are due to habit. These habits cause us to fail because they are neither general nor specific enough for the new problems we are trying to solve. Furthermore, we fail in applying habits because we include ourselves in the problem. Various mental blocks stand between us and the solution. We can overcome these habit obstacles by understanding how problems are solved. We help ourselves when we try to understand the obstacles to our thinking and deliberately try to overcome them. To this end we must consciously develop those creative traits which maximize the probability of finding new combinations of ideas. Of necessity, the information presented in this book on these areas is brief. Material is currently available elsewhere to expand the designer's understanding of these fields.

Discernment and Selectivity . . .

"It's certainly an interesting linkage, but I'd like to point out that you could replace it with a pulley."

In addition to these more or less passive suggestions, we can employ more active methods.

For the Individual

Getting started, first of all, increases our interest and motivation. Then we can set deadlines and quotas for ourselves. By setting aside definite times and places consistent with our personal habits, we increase

How can such deep-imprinted images sleep in us at times, till a word, a sound, awake them? Lessing.

our ability to concentrate and intensify our awareness of the problem. If we use a plan or system (for example, the present one) to build upon as we see fit, we will free our mind of some of the more routine tasks. Perhaps by warming up our "thinking machinery" with some marginal tasks related to the problem, or warming up on such idea and association getters as may prove useful, we will stimulate our interest in what has to be done.

Working in a permissive atmosphere greatly increases interest and motivation. While we cannot always do this, it is the ideal we should look for and the environment we are most apt to succeed in. Such a permissive atmosphere consists of freedom of expression to try out ideas, satisfaction with the job, effective means of communication, and mutual respect and encouragement from colleagues and superiors.

We should prod our interest and motivation even when failures occur. This perseverance is easier when we realize that failures are an essential part of success. We must be willing, therefore, to take a chance and gamble. We must realize that *all* solutions are a compromise between conflicting requirements and that excessive idealism will stand in the way of our making a decision.

We should study our thinking habits thoroughly —that is, when and where do we work best. Some of us do our most useful work in the early morning while others work best in the afternoon. Some find their ideas coming when they are fresh; others when they are somewhat worn down. We should encourage the conditions under which illumination occurs and should be willing to postpone further work on the problem after we have thoroughly saturated ourselves with information and have not been successful. When this happens we should try another task in the hope that our subconscious mind will succeed.

We must work hard at changing our old habits in all phases of problem solution. We should sit down and deliberately try to define problems, find more unusual bits of information, search for more remote and obscure methods of analysis, and practice association of ideas. This is difficult work at first but eventually it becomes a very interesting and stimulating game.

Perhaps the most essential rule which may be suggested for intensifying interest in the job is: postpone the evaluation of ideas. The designer must learn to separate the task of thinking up from the task of judging. If we do not divorce these two functions, we develop the habit of approaching problems with a negative attitude and soon begin to feel that nothing is ever possible.

Since our past experiences with problems and situations is the basis for solving our present problems, it is important that we increase our store of such raw materials. It will do no good to memorize a lot of facts but it is necessary that we be exposed to various situations and understand the associations involved. Such experiences may be obtained by travel, by the use of puzzles and games, by hobbies and fine arts, by intensive and extensive reading, by writing, and by solving various problems. In each of these it is not wise that the designer confine himself to too narrow a range of interests since the truly creative solution will come about by association of very obscure and different ideas.

We can assist our association of ideas by writing down various thoughts and observations. This recording of information frees the mind from having to remember. It is disconcerting to be conscious that some information is available for the solution and then not be able to recall its precise nature. Other specific devices are useful in facilitating association, and particularly useful in the analysis and synthesis phases of problem solving. These are as follows: check-lists, input-output technique, brainstorming, attribute listing, and others.

Also see *Applied Imagination,* Alex F. Osborn, New York: Scribner, 1953, 1957.

For Groups

While total problem solving is indeed an individual task there are certain phases during which the group may be used with some success. Since there is a current fad for solving problems by group effort, rather than individually, it is well to understand what part groups can or cannot play in solving problems.

We have seen that the process of divergent thinking is one of association. The greater the number of associations we can make, the more likely we are to have a creative solution to our problem. The process of tying together various ideas is complicated by our own experiences, and our own preconceptions. Along the way we run into blocks which hinder us from seeing ideas in a new light and from applying old solutions to new situations. If then, some means can be found which will help circumvent these mental blocks a greater number of associations should be possible.

Many ideas grow better when transplanted into another mind than in the one where they sprang up. Oliver W. Holmes.

If a number of people are used to synthesize solutions we have many points of view, and a multiplicity of experiences which may be used for solutions. Hence a greater number of associations are possible. The ideas of one individual may be used as steppingstones for the ideas of others. Based upon chance alone, the group has the advantage. Suppose we have a given problem which only one-fourth of the individuals can solve on an individual basis. If we assemble four subjects from this population sample, only one in the group will need to have the solution in order that the group will solve the problem. Therefore, with this number in the group the chance of solving the problem will not be one out of four but seven out of ten. This is assuming no interaction between the members of the group and no change in individual abilities while a member of the group.

Osborn has stated that the group method will produce up to 44 per cent more ideas than the same individuals working by themselves. The group requires less elapsed time to solve a given problem but is less efficient in terms of the total number of hours involved. Perhaps the greatest benefit arises from the fact that it gives the people within an organization an opportunity to express themselves in public. "In our company," says one high executive, "an executive is often rated more highly if he makes no mistakes than if he suggests lots of ideas. If brainstorming can give higher place to the idea man than to the careful man, we might all be better off."

See *Creative Discussion,* R. C. Cartright and G. L. Hinds.

However, certain disadvantages are inherent in group effort. As the size of the group increases, so does the number of viewpoints, the number of habits and preconceived ideas, and the number of blocks which may be thrown in the way. The group is not always as highly motivated as the individual might be. It has been found that the group, placing extremely high emphasis on agreement, will tend to kill the opinions of the minority and tend toward mediocrity. In their attempts to compromise, the group will likely end up with all the disadvantages and none of the advantages of the solutions. The ideas which an individual might develop in the privacy of his own office are often killed before they may emerge.

So by studying the picture carefully, we may conclude that group ideation can be successful *if applied in the proper place.* To expect a number of people to get together and mutually solve the total problem in all its aspects, is merely wishful thinking. Group methods and particularly brainstorming apply only to some very narrow aspects of problem solving. Principally, they may be used for divergent thinking. Once a problem has been defined and narrowed down and the pertinent information analyzed, a group may get together to try to synthesize possible solutions. After that, it is usually up to the individual to evaluate each solution, to analyze it further, and to check out the results, and finally to sell it to whomever may be concerned. The group method may also be used to a lesser degree to think up all of the problem situations that may be involved in a solution of a given design, to think up various sources of information, and perhaps to think up various criteria for evaluation. In each case, however, the thinking-up phase is only a portion of the total work. The group method is no panacea for our design problems. *There is no way of avoiding individual responsibility for the complete solution.*

In order to give the group the best chance for functioning and best opportunity for thinking up ideas, a number of rules should be observed. The group should contain people with a diversity of talents and interests so that the associations are maximized. They should be tied together by some common interest or motivation which is usually furnished by the organization. They should possess mutual respect for each other and a high degree of intellectual honesty.

Brainstorming

See *Brainstorming,* by Charles H. Clark.

Perhaps the most common group method is that of brainstorming originated by Alex Osborn. It has been successfully employed with groups up to fifty in number. In this method the problem has been narrowed down and is rather specific in nature. After the group has been carefully selected, has been assembled, and has been given the problem, certain rules are proposed. They are: 1. Judicial judgment is ruled out. Criticism of ideas must be withheld until later. 2. "Free wheeling" is welcome. The wilder the ideas, the better: it is easier to tame down than to think up. 3. Quantity is wanted. The greater the number of ideas the more the likelihood of a good one. 4. Combination and improvement are sought. In addition to contributing ideas of their own, panel members should suggest how suggestions by others could be turned into better ideas, or how two or more ideas could be combined into a still better idea.

The results of a brainstorming session used to synthesize solutions to engineering problems should help us to understand the method. The results of such a session involving 70 graduates of MIT who participated at a brainstorming dinner are as follows:

> **"How many ideas can you think of to make a universal landing gear that will be adaptable for use on water, snow, and land?"**

1. Expandable rubber hull, with wheels on side.
2. Hydraulic attached to separate gears for each condition.
3. Large enough wheels to act as floats—brake wheels for snow.
4. One large cylindrical wheel.
5. Skids on amphibian hull.
6. Tripod skid arrangement.
7. Track-laying scheme rotating with buoyant hub.
8. Reinforced body for direct skid.
9. Wheels with hydrofoils.
10. Car brush effect for all surfaces.
11. Grease injector on skids for land operation.
12. Skid float with retractable wheel.

13. Plastic for reducing friction on skid.
14. Helicopter effect on gear.
15. Reverse jet—no gear.
16. Foam protection of hull to absorb shock.
17. Vertical air jets or rockets to replace run area.
18. Large plastic roller.
19. Elliptical roller which can be rotated 90°.
20. Use normal wheels or skids for land or snow—inflate pontoons for water.
21. Lay down foam mat from plane—by spray.
22. Rotate cabin 90° exposing skids.
23. Rotate landing mechanism.
24. Combine toboggan and hull float—replaceable bottom.
25. Wheels with cup-shaped hubs—rotate 90° for water.
26. Pilots with big feet.

"You'll have to call back. He's in a brainstorming session."

It should be noted from the preceding list that the number of very worthwhile solutions is relatively small. In general, the solution of the problem requires only one acceptable idea. We should observe that some of the associations are remote and not likely to be thought up by ourselves in individual ideation.

Brainstorming may be used in those areas involving divergent thinking. Its advantages lie in the motivation and contagion generated by the group, in the multiplicity of associations which are possible because of the varying experiences, and the interactions between members of the group affording an opportunity to build upon another individual's ideas. Its disadvantages lie in the fact that it is not applicable to all aspects of problem solving, that the group may play down the opinions of the minority, that the group may be in error, and that the impracticality of many of the ideas may stymie the flow of solutions.

It should be noted that the functioning of the group is very similar to the manner in which an individual solves a problem. Based upon these problem-solving principles, a number of other group methods have been developed. The Phillips 66 Buzz Session method attempts to use large groups by dividing them into smaller groups of four to six persons. These groups are then given five to ten minutes to think up solutions for a stated problem, and to narrow the list to one best idea for the group. The Arthur D. Little (consulting engineering firm) group technique or Gordon method is a more sophisticated and complicated way of employing the various talents of a number of experts. There are a number of modifications of this method but the goal behind each is to improve the association ability of the group by the gradual introduction of the problem itself. This method requires more careful selection of the panelists and appears to be exceptionally applicable to the solution of design problems.

These group methods have been more or less successfully employed by various organizations. At one "clinic," engineers and doctors got together to explore by brainstorming the potential of new instrument techniques for measuring and diagnosing physical and chemical variables in the human brain. At Arthur D. Little Company, the methods have been used to develop new products of various manufacturing companies, particularly those producing a product used by the general public. Although it is possible that a goodly number of these organizatons have participated in brainstorming sessions because it is a current fad or a currently acceptable tool of business, certainly many of them have benefitted in an increase of ideas and improvement in relations between employees.

Creativity and the Group Supervisor

The key figure in inspiring high achievement and maximum creative performance from engineers and scientists is the immediate supervisor. His attitudes can either stimulate or stifle potential creativity. The following material is a summary of a recent book published by Industrial Relations News. The men who provided the information for this survey, work in creativity research, teach creative thinking courses, serve as consultants to industry, or direct advanced research and development work.

The ideal supervisor should be *creative*. Primarily, he should be a creative person himself. "He understands the thrill of creation by having experienced it himself." He should *understand the creative process*. He should have an articulate insight into the nature of thinking. Rather than trying to eliminate the trials and frustrations of the creative process, the wise leader must try to understand the cycle, to nurse projects along, and to give the proper encouragement at the proper time. He should therefore *understand creative temperaments* and have an objective but always compassionate understanding of creative people, their temperaments and motivations.

A creative supervisor must have *high technical competence.* Technology has developed to such a degree of complexity and difficulty that it takes an active, inquisitive, and expansively interested person who studies, reads, and experiments in many diverse fields to make significant scientific advancements. The creative scientist certainly has to be a specialist and thoroughly versed in one field. But this has to be counterbalanced with a versatility of experience and knowledge. He has to be a specialist and *also* a generalist.

He must, furthermore, *inspire and encourage.* He should be a man who has contagious enthusiasm for research, who constantly encourages and stimulates his people to come up with new imaginative approaches, welcomes innovation and change, and takes a lively and active interest in their efforts and problems.

The creative supervisor should *safeguard areas of freedom* and take great pains not to dictate approaches to problems but rather to define the ultimate research goal in a general way. In this way he encourages individual initiative and provides the necessary permissiveness. Suggestions and ideas should be welcomed and individuals should be allowed to relax their binding habit patterns and "let themselves go." Individual initiative is lacking among scientists and engineers in many companies because they never have been impressed with the desirability of showing any. The supervisor must indicate to his creative people what is expected of them, what they are permitted to do, and the areas where they may exercise independent judgment and freedom.

The creative supervisor should boost the self-confidence of his aides. Fear of criticism, fear of superior's or colleagues' opinions or disapprovals, doubts about his own abilities, fear of appearing too revolutionary or unusual—all these feelings can inhibit or suppress creativity. The supervisor should have confidence in his own ability. When the group embarks on a new problem, he should be ready to take the calculated risks involved and be able to maintain a positive and optimistic approach toward the problem and any solutions. Knowing when to ask stimulating and searching questions and when to listen, a supervisor encourages both thinking and confident rehearsal of any ideas that occur. It is here that his ability to suspend critical judgment is put to the test. Nothing can inhibit ideas more than judgment or evaluation applied prematurely in the process of creative ideation. A basic optimism and a stubborn refusal to give up are two very important qualities in the creative supervisor's personality makeup. He also bolsters self-confidence by *respecting others.* He should recognize an original concept and recognize unselfishly the merits of the ideas his team suggests. He should be goal-oriented rather than status-oriented. He should be more interested in seeing the problem solved than in gaining personal glory.

A supervisor must be a *tactful critic* and *give credit early.* He should be able to convince members of his group that they will be properly identified for their work and be given credit. He should *assign responsibility skillfully.* He should know his groups so well as individuals that he can make assignments that will conform to the personalities, interests, and abilities of the individuals. He should furthermore *control lightly.* After breaking the project down into individual assignments and properly assigning them to individual workers, the supervisor should leave each creative worker either completely alone or exert minimum direct influence on him. He should make sure that his instructions do not incorporate his own ideas about the approach to be used in tackling the problem.

The following story is taken from a commencement address by Charles F. Kettering at the General Motors Institute:

HABITS IN ENGINEERING

Lubricating oils are very old, and some time ago at Cornell University there was developed a lubricating testing machine based on a railroad journal. Many tests had been run, a lot of tables plotted out, and six thousand pounds per square inch of projected area of the bearing was the highest that they could go with the best lubricating oils then available. We had built a small testing machine at our laboratories and our figures checked very well with this.

Now what more could you ask?

So I said, "Well, let's just try an experiment. Let's suppose that the lubricating oil testing machine is a dangerous weapon. It belongs to your worst enemy, and he can kill you and your family with it. But you can pick the lubricant for it. What would you recommend if you were picking the poorest thing in the world to lubricate it with? What would you specify?"

We all thought about it, and finally picked a material called monochlormethyl ether, which is practically the same as is used to put you to sleep when you are going to have a surgical operation. It is so thin it has no viscosity at all. You can pour it on your hand and blow on it and it is all gone. You couldn't pour it in a warm machine as a liquid, it would evaporate at once, so we took the cap off the ether can, soldered a tube on it, ran the tube over to the bearing machine and sealed it into the oil hole. Then we put a warm towel around the can and the vapors went through the tube to the bearing. Since there was no liquid in the bearing it must run absolutely dry.

We had made bets on how long it would last—how much pressure it would take. One man had nerve enough to guess 150 pounds. That was the highest. We started to load up the machine very gently and carefully, and to make a long story short, we ran out of weights at 30,000 pounds. Everybody was amazed; they said, "It can't be." But we tried it over and over again, and we got some more weights. I think it stuck up around 36,000 pounds —five or six times the load of the best oil.

We brought the oil engineers in and showed it to them. They said, "The only thing that makes us sore is that we didn't do it. This is our business, not yours."

"But," I said, "you couldn't have done it. You have graded oils for so long on their viscosity that you would have fired anybody who proposed using something like this, that didn't have any viscosity feel to it."

Well, that was the beginning of the so-called extreme pressure lubrication which came just about the time we were developing the hypoid gears, and you couldn't have run hypoid gears if it hadn't been for these lubricants. There are many things that you couldn't do today if it wasn't for these lubricants.

Now what did we do? All that had been done in lubricating oils before that was to test the affinity of one molecule of oil for another. This is called viscosity. When you put pressure on them, you found that you pushed them apart and you had no lubrication. But the oils with no viscosity at all formed a chemical bond more like the nap on plush, and this took much more pressure to break through than did the viscosity film. It completely changed the concept of what you could do with lubricating oils.

SUMMARY

Habit, which has been used in solving past problems, prevents our finding creative solutions. Because of habit, we fail to recognize difficulties, improperly define the problem, neglect significant information, fail to distinguish relationships among the data, fail to assemble ideas, and put solutions into effect. Mental blocks arise because of our environment, because of stress and frustration from fear of the unknown, and because of over- or under-motivation. We ourselves are our greatest obstacle to a satisfactory solution.

If an engineer is to come up with unusual solutions to his problems and if he is to overcome, to some extent at least, the emotional, cultural and perceptual blocks which are thrown in his way, he must develop or improve the following personal traits: self-

confidence, constructive nonconformity, willingness to take calculated risks, openness to experience, active curiosity, sensitivity to problems, high motivation, knowledge of fundamentals, flexibility, tolerance for ambiguity, intellectual integrity, ability to toy with ideas, ability to suspend critical judgment, ability to think in images, ability to think in analogies.

These techniques for encouraging creative designs may be used either individually or as a group. While designing is principally an individual activity, certain phases such as thinking up problems, exchanging information, synthesizing ideas, and evaluating solutions may be augmented by group efforts. The group, in using brainstorming or other techniques, should follow the same recommendations as that for the individual.

The capable designer often not only is part of a group but must frequently supervise a team project. The ideal creative supervisor is a pleasant, easy-to-get-along-with person who has high standards of integrity, and who can be, depending upon the circumstances, either serious and sincere or humorous and relaxed. He is patient, tolerant, and extremely flexible in both thinking and acting. He feels that he can take nothing for granted and has an "openness to experience" in that he is continuously open to the overwhelming complex and contradictory ramifications of experience. He has the ability to receive conflicting information without forcing closure on the situation. His outstanding skill should be in the area of communication. He should have the ability to express problems clearly, ability to guide by questioning, ability to lead and arbitrate decisions, ability to ask intelligent, searching questions that stimulate, stir, and encourage thinking and work. On him falls the responsibility to maintain open, effective communica-

tions within his department and with other departments in the company and with management.

Active methods for overcoming habit blocks may be employed. The designer's motivation may be increased by setting quotas and deadlines and by forcing himself to just start anywhere. He should work in a permissive atmosphere and should remember that failure is an essential part of trying to find solutions. He should study his own thinking habits, expanding on the phases discussed so as to match his own personality. He should attempt to develop and encourage his subconscious mind in incubation and illumination. The writing down of ideas frees the mind from having to remember. The designer's store of basic concepts and experiences (not facts and figures) must be increased. He must learn to separate the thinking-up phases from evaluation.

APPENDIX MAIN DIVISIONS	
A. Check-List for Problem Solving	D. Creative Problems
B. General Problems	E. "The Innocents Beguiled" from *Tom Sawyer*
C. Design Problems	F. Bibliography

Appendix A

Check-List For Problem Solving

EVALUATION OF DESIGN ABILITIES AND PROCEDURES:

1. **Recognition and definition:**

_____Courage and drive in attacking unfamiliar, complex problems
_____Understanding of terms in given problem
_____Understanding of specifications and limits of the problem, both stated and implied
_____Ability to consider these limits continually when solving other phases of the problem
_____Necessary effort expended in reorganizing the problem in order to gain a better understanding of the goals
_____Ability to subdivide complex problems into workable parts
_____Ability to focus attention on each problem separately
_____Use of a plan or method for solution of the problem

2. **Preparation:**

_____Understanding of the accuracy of the information acquired
_____Thoroughness and completeness of accumulated information
_____Ability to make simplifying assumptions
_____Willingness to make logical assumptions for missing information
_____Understanding of sufficient information to attack problem
_____Understanding of basic concepts and tools of engineering

3. **Analysis:**

_____Ability to translate difficult terms in the problem into simpler and more familiar terms
_____Thoroughness of understanding of interrelationships among the variables

_____Understanding of implications of the ideas
_____Ability to select relevant information to analyze
_____Skill in associating this information with the problem to be solved
_____Ability to manipulate unfamiliar terms and ideas
_____Skill in making and using hypotheses
_____Confidence in knowledge and abilities possessed
_____Persistence in attempting to solve a given sub-problem without jumping to another part
_____Skill in considering important details of the problem
_____Persistence despite many external considerations
_____Skill in using solutions to old problems but not being limited by them
_____Ability to persevere with original plan of action as difficulties are encountered
_____Patience and skill in making checks on reasoning and conclusions made
_____Ability to maintain objective attitude despite personal opinions and habits
_____Confidence in ability to reason and solve the problem

4. **Synthesis:**

_____Ability to adapt a functional principle from a radically different area
_____Ability to utilize combinations of principles
_____Skill in mentally manipulating solutions from radically different areas by changing one or more of the variables
_____Ability to visualize ideas particularly in new situations

5. **Evaluation:**

_____Ability to find all considerations and situations
_____Skill in avoiding "feelings" or "impressions" about which is the best solution
_____Ability to evaluate and decide despite the unattractiveness of some of the solutions
_____Ability to substantiate a selection and avoid guesswork
_____Skill in continuing analysis until evaluation and selection are possible
_____Ability to weigh choices, to winnow lesser solutions
_____Courage in deciding between alternatives and drawing definite conclusions
_____Confidence in the correctness of the solution
_____Skill in avoiding the inclusion of personal value-patterns in judging the ideas

6. **Presentation:**

_____Ability to implement the decision with effective action
_____Skill in conveying the information to others
_____Patience and skill in changing the habit patterns of others as may be required
_____Understanding of motivations and goals of others

Appendix B

General Problems

The following problems are intended to show the application of the procedures discussed. With the knowledge and experience possessed by a freshman engineering student all should be workable without recourse to any reference material.

1. To promote the sale of new cars selling at $1500, the manufacturing company offers its salesmen a bonus of $100 for the first, $110 for the second, $120 for the third, etc., car sold in excess of the first 50 cars sold per month. The regular commission is 10 per cent for each car. How many cars must each salesman sell a month in order that the company may make a maximum gross profit?
2. A light is to be placed on a wall so as to illuminate a desk S feet from the wall. Assuming that the illumination varies inversely as the square of the distance and directly as the sine of the angle of inclination of the rays on the desk, how high above the desk should the light be placed?
3. Two motorboats start at the same time from the same dock. One travels in the direction 75° east of south at 40 mph. In what direction must the other travel at 50 mph in order to be due north of the first?
4. Two beach lights are due east of a dock at distances of 200 yards and 2000 yards. An observer on a boat due south of the dock finds at one point that the difference in the directions of the lights is 45 degrees. After proceeding toward the dock a certain distance, he again finds the difference in direction of the lights to be 45 degrees. What is the distance traveled between the two points of observation?
5. The present population of New York City is 6,000,000. Its birth rate is 3 per cent per year; its death rate, 2 per cent per year. How many people will

be born in New York in the next 50 years if the rates remain unchanged?

6. The electric lights of a city go out at the rate of 0.5 per cent per month. Because of shortage of bulbs only 10,000 can be replaced each month. If the initial number of lights is 10,000,000, in how many months will the supply be sufficient to replace the bulbs going out each month?
7. What is the area of a parallelogram (prove solution)?
8. What is the cosine rule for a triangle (formula for finding the length of one side if the other two sides are given and their included angle)?
9. In the equation $d^4=Ad^2+Bd$, if d is length, what are the dimensions of A and B?
10. The highest and lowest points in the United States are in California within sight of each other and only 86 mi. apart. They are the crest of Mt. Whitney, 14,496 ft. above sea level and Bad Water, the terminal pool of Amargosa River, 276 ft. below sea level. What angle does a line joining these points make with the horizontal plane?
11. Two shafts are coupled by means of a belt around two pulleys. The driving shaft has a 24 in. pulley and the driven shaft has a 36 in. pulley. The taut and slack sides of the belt are under tensions of 70 and 10 lb. respectively. Find the torque exerted at each pulley.
12. A clock loses ten minutes each hour. If the clock is set at 12 o'clock noon, what is the correct time when the clock reads 3:00 P.M. the same day?
    (a) 3:36 P.M.
    (b) 3:30 P.M.
    (c) 2:36 P.M.
    (d) 3:40 P.M.
    (e) None of the above
13. You have a nickel, a dime, a quarter and a fifty-cent piece. A clerk shows you several articles, each a different price and any one of which you could purchase with one or more of your coins without receiving change. What is the largest number of articles he could have shown you? (*a*) 8 (*b*) 10 (*c*) 13 (*d*) 15 (*e*) 21
14. A computer was told that a survey had been made of a certain rectangular field but the dimensions had been lost. An assistant remembered that if the field had been 100 ft. longer and 25 ft. narrower, the area would have been increased 2,500 sq. ft., and that if it had been 100 ft. shorter and 50 ft. wider, the area would have been decreased 5,000 sq. ft. What was the area of the field and what were its dimensions?
15. A flat-bottomed scow is built with vertical sides and straight sloping ends. Its length on deck is 80 ft., and on the bottom, 65 ft.; its width is 20 ft., and its vertical depth is 12 ft. How much water will it draw if it weighs 250 tons?
16. A box is to be constructed from a piece of zinc 20 in. square by cutting equal squares from each corner and turning up the zinc to form the sides. What is the volume of the largest box that can be so constructed?

17. Two planes leave Cleveland for Jacksonville, a distance of 900 miles. The four-motored plane (A) travels at a ground speed of 90 mph faster than the two-motored plane (B). Plane A arrives in Jacksonville 2 hr. 15 min. ahead of plane B. What were the respective ground speeds of the two planes?
18. Prove that the opposite angles formed by two intersecting lines are equal.
19. Design slide rules to perform the following operations: add, subtract, multiply. Do so in such a manner that the answer can always be read opposite an arrow at one end of the scale similar to the system used in dividing.
20. Point B is 9 in. due east of A. Point C is 8 in. west of A, 3 in. south of A and 4 in. below A. Is the distance AB greater than, less than, or equal to the distance AC, or is the problem incapable of solution?
21. The center of gravity of a plane area may be defined as the point on which the area may be balanced if cut out of a piece of cardboard of uniform thickness. What then is the center of gravity of a triangle?
22. Given two straight lines, A and B. If A passes through the coordinate points $x=1$, $y=0$, and $x=20$, $y=10$, and if line B passes through the points $x=0$, $y=4$, and $x=11$, $y=0$, what is the point common to both lines?
23. Determine the relationship between the sine of the sum of two angles and the functions of the angles themselves.
24. A certain geometric figure is defined as the path of point C of triangle ABC when length AB=constant and the sum of AC and BC=constant. Find means for constructing this figure.
25. What is the sum of the numbers from 1 to 50? from 75 to 320?
    [This is the problem (from 1 to 10) solved by Gauss when he was only about 6 years old. By using a simple method, he was suspected of cheating.]
26. What is the area of a trapezoid?
27. For the multiplication $CDE \times AB = FGHIJ$ what are the digits (1 through 0) represented by the letters A through J if each digit is used only once?

Appendix C

Design Problems

The following problems illustrate the application of the procedure to complex areas which require subdivision into sub-problems of function, breakage, maintenance, and the like: When desirable information has been omitted, reasonable values should be assumed. (These problems and others may be found in "Why Don't They Research and Develop," *Product Engineering* magazine and "Inventions Wanted by the Armed Forces," U.S. Department of Commerce, Office of Technical Services, National Inventors Council.

1. Emerson is said to have made a statement concerning the relationship of the designing of a better mousetrap to a path being beaten to the door. Using this method of problem solving, design a better mousetrap.
2. Design a mechanical computer to solve the following mathematical equation.
$$y=Ax^2+Bx$$
3. "This company is now the leading manufacturer of gasoline-powered lawn mowers. We have produced these mowers for the past 50 years and enjoy the reputation of producing the most reliable and most economical mower manufactured today. We are now desirous of diversifying our production. We would like to produce a 16-inch chain saw to retail from $150 to $180. It is expected that eventually we will manufacture a complete line of such saws to meet competition."
4. Design a self-editing conference recorder. Continuous recording takes much time during playback. Summary or highlight recording interrupts the flow of a conference and is not feasible during lectures. Intermittent recording requires rare foresight to capture important statements. A magnetic tape loop which is continuously recording and erasing and has a pickup head connected to a second tape recorder would permit automatic editing. A touch of a button

after each important point would transfer the stored words from the loop to the auxiliary recorder. A battery-operated transistorized unit is feasible.

5. Design an indicator-recorder for very slow linear speeds (down to 0.5 in. per minute). Many machines have indication or control of feeds at those speeds, but the usual gear drives, tachometer generators and the like when multiplied sufficiently to record and indicate on standard instruments, are so inaccurate as to be valueless.

   How about a vernier arrangement in which two sets of accurately spaced grids are placed closely together? The line density would be almost identical —say, 100 per in. on one and 99 per in. on the other. Capacitance or inductance would change through a measurable cycle every 0.0001 in. or at 0.5 in./min.; 83 cps. A simple frequency meter would then read in linear speed if suitably calibrated.

6. Design automobile headlights which point the same way the wheels do. Several systems have been tried to accomplish this, but the linkages get too complex for reasonable cost. How about a simple on-off type servo system operating off a small contact switch?

7. Design a dashboard-mounted gauge giving gas consumption in miles per gallon. A driver could modify his speed to establish most economical operation for long trips. The device would have to be accurate and react very quickly to changes in speed.

8. Design an automatic wheel balancer for automobile wheels. Ideally, this device should be inexpensive enough to be included on every wheel—say on the standard wheel-mounting bolts in the hub cap. It should adjust imbalance automatically and continuously during driving. This would eliminate frequent wheel maintenance to take care of wear.

9. Find some final solution to the hydraulic-system leakage problem. After so many years of trying all sorts of metal-to-metal and rubber-sealed fittings, systems still leak—and will, so long as power is transmitted by a thin fluid. The National Inventors Council suggests using a new material having the stress distribution properties of water or oil: "It should be resistant to leakage, that is, a solid or semi-solid. Very soft rubbers approach this requirement." Now combine this with pulse power and you have a system with no leakage.

10. Design a small spot welder, about the size of a pair of pliers, for hobbyists, model-makers, etc.

11. Design a plastic mercury-bulb thermometer. Glass thermometers are fragile, relatively expensive when accurate, and somewhat difficult to read at any distance. Although plastic would have a higher coefficient of expansion than glass, a low-expansion metal insert could be molded around the mercury reservoir, and the stem similarly reinforced by an insert. For clinical mouth thermometers plastic would be less grating on the teeth and less likely to break because of its flexibility.

12. Design a ball-type worm drive. It would have all the advantages of low friction loss (serious in worm drives) as well as high gear reduction. Note

the need for careful enclosure design for the circulating balls, plus attention to thrust loads on the worm.

13. Develop an electron tube telltale in some way to indicate when a tube filament is open-circuited. Filament glow could be focused on a fluorescent spot at the top of the tube envelope and the color might be an indication of tube condition. Some similar means should be developed to indicate tube shorts as well—to eliminate the problem of carrying maybe 25 TV set tubes to the local radioman at regular intervals.
14. Design an additional typewriter key to eradicate mistakes. In retracted position it might be immersed in a quick-drying, ink-dissolving solution. A second, blotting key may also be needed.
15. Design a mechanical brake for small power boats, controlled by a foot pedal. Cables could pull a plastic or metal dish below the stern to stop forward motion.
16. Design for soft-drink machines, a system of cooling the bottles on demand rather than all the time. The cost of electrical power, on hot summer nights when the machines are not in use and on days when drinks aren't selling, could be completely eliminated. How about a CO_2 bottle with a jet outlet near the exit chute for the necessary quick chill?
17. Design a small, battery-operated automobile. It should have a 50-mile range per charge, 30 mph top speed, be rechargeable off house current and priced from $200 to $500. It would serve admirably for shopping and for husband and child pick-up and delivery. Result: a lot less air polution, fewer traffic deaths, and less wear and tear on the family pocketbook.
18. Develop a vacuum cleaner that is not limited to atmospheric pressure. A maximum pressure differential of 14.7 psi is hardly adequate for some industrial applications.
19. Devise a simple method of locating breaks in underwater cables. It is suggested that each repeater station be equipped with an oscillator and transducer that would transmit sound waves through water. When a break occurred, sonic generators in the two repeater stations adjacent to the break would be set off. Shipboard detectors could spot the break quickly and repair the cable in the usual way.
20. Devise a scheme to prevent skidding of the wheels on cars or trucks when the brakes are applied on icy pavement.
21. Design a self-service gasoline pump. Credit-card customers could drive up, insert the credit card to operate the pump and the pump would issue a receipt after filling.
22. Design a centrifugal oil filter for automobiles.

Appendix D

Creative Problems

The following problems should serve to test the engineer's ability to get off beaten paths and to exhibit creativity:

1. While a ship is floating in a canal lock, some of the cargo accidentally slides overboard and sinks to the bottom of the lock. If the gates remained closed during this time, what happened to the water level in the lock? Did it go up, down, or remain at constant level?
2. Two ships are 100 miles apart and traveling at 20 miles per hour toward each other. A sea gull flies from the deck of one ship directly toward the second ship at 50 miles per hour. Upon meeting the second ship he immediately turns around and flies toward ship No. 1. Upon meeting this ship he again turns around and flies toward ship No. 2. Thus he continues to fly between the ships until they sail adjacent to each other. By this time how far did the gull fly?
3. Find the missing numbers for the following equation:

   (— 1 — — —) (4 1 7) = 9 — — — 0 5 7
4. A machine has the capacity to produce 200 thingumajigs and 150 gismos each 8-hour day. If the profit is 20¢ per thingumajig and 50¢ per gismo and if the manufacturing time is .02 and .04 hours respectively, how many of each item should be scheduled for the machine per day so as to maximize the profit?
5. There are *two* solutions to the following problem. Find them both: A man walks one mile south, one mile west, and one mile north, and finds himself where he started. Where did this take place?

6. Several miles of electrical cable containing 13 wires were buried before it was realized that they were not color-coded. Determine a way in which one man could identify the wires with a minimum of travel between the ends and with simple equipment.
7. Explain why the image of your hand in a mirror is reversed from left to right but not top to bottom.
8. Can an obtuse triangle be divided into smaller acute triangles? All the smaller triangles must have acute angles.
9. Determine the missing digits:

$$\frac{X\,X\,X\,X\,X\,X\,X\,X}{X\,X\,X} = X\,X\,8\,X\,X$$

10.

You are in a magnetically shielded room. You have two bars of iron and no other equipment or apparatus. One of the bars is a permanent magnet with poles at opposite ends, the other is formed of soft iron.

Q. How can you determine which bar is magnetized?

(*From CGS Laboratories, Inc.*)

The answer to this problem is straightforward and positive. It does not involve rubbing the bars, striking them together, or suspending them.

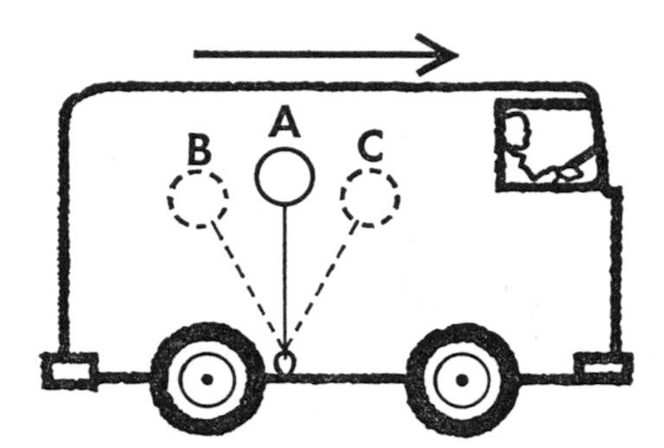

11.

A van-type truck is completely sealed. A balloon filled with hydrogen is buoyed upward by the air in the truck and is restrained by a string secured to the floor of the truck. The truck is then accelerated continuously in the direction of the arrow.

Q. Relative to the truck does the balloon remain in position *A*? Move toward position *B*? Move toward position *C*?

In the problem about the balloon in the truck, if you picked positions *B* or *A* you overlooked something.

(*From CGS Laboratories, Inc.*)

12.

A bomb is filled with air at atmospheric pressure. A candle in the bomb under ordinary conditions consumes O_2 at such a rate that the quantity of air in the bomb would cause the candle to burn for one minute. The candle is ignited at the instant the bomb is released from a height of 20,000 feet, to fall freely toward the earth.

Neglecting wind currents and assuming the bomb to remain oriented as shown, will the candle continue to burn for (A) Less than one minute? (B) One minute? (C) More than one minute? Why?

(*From CGS Laboratories, Inc.*)

13.

We have a space ship which is stationary in space and outside the influence of any other body. Two dogs, Alpha and Beta, occupy the space ship and propel it through space by this means: Alpha at one end of the space ship has a large boulder that he throws to Beta in the other end of the ship. This obviously causes the ship to move in the direction of the arrow. Alpha then rotates a wheel (A) causing the ship to rotate end for end. When the ship has rotated through 180° he stops the wheel and Beta throws the rock back to Alpha, obviously moving the ship further in the direction of the arrow. Repeating this process the dogs continue to transport themselves through space!!

Q. What, if anything, is *fundamentally* amiss?

(*From CGS Laboratories, Inc.*)

14. Given: 100 boxes of miniature ball bearings

    each box contains 100 bearings
    each bearing weighs .01 pounds except for one box containing bearings all of which are either 10 per cent heavy or 10 per cent light
    all bearings, including those out-of-weight, are identical in appearance
    each box also weighs .01 pounds

Determine, with one reading only of a very sensitive scale, which box contains the out-of-weight bearings and whether they are heavy or light.

15. A little boy carried his pet pigeon in a large closed box. He continually pounded on the side of the box so as to keep the bird flying inside. He insisted this made the box lighter. Do you agree with him? If the box had been covered only with a very light screen, would this have made any difference?

16. There is a common and simple toy on the market called the "Tippy-Top." Its shape is hemi-spherical with a stem attached for spinning. When the stem is rapidly twisted and the top allowed to spin on the rounded bottom, it will soon turn upside down to spin on the stem.

    Explain the physical principles behind this device which permits it to spin upside down. Be careful about obvious answers.

    After the reader has attempted the solution and checked out any ideas, he is referred to the *Mathematical Gazette,* Vol. XI, No. 334, Dec. 1, 1956.

17. A table has a frictionless surface with a small hole in the center. Through this hole is placed a string, and a weight is attached to each end. The weights are selected so that the upper weight may be rotated so that its movement describes a circle about the hole in the table; the lower weight being sufficient to oppose the force exerted on the string by the rotation of the upper weight. Since the surface of the table (and the hole) is frictionless, a state of equilibrium exists.

    Q. Describe what happens if the lower weight is pulled down a few inches.

    (*From CGS Laboratories, Inc.*)

Answers to some of these problems:

1. The level would go down. Carefully study Archimedes.
2. 125 miles. Simple logic is easier than algebra.
3. 21921×417=
4. 100 thingumajigs, 150 gismos for a daily profit of $95.

Additional problems of this nature together with sources for other problems may be found in *Mathematical Puzzles and Diversions,* by Martin Gardner, New York: Simon and Schuster, 1959.

Appendix E
The Innocents Beguiled

Condensed Version From TOM SAWYER by MARK TWAIN

Saturday morning was come, and all the summer world was bright and fresh, and brimming with life. There was a song in every heart; and if the heart was young the music issued at the lips. There was cheer in every face and a spring in every step.

Tom appeared on the sidewalk with a bucket of whitewash and a long-handled brush. He surveyed the fence, and all gladness left him and a deep melancholy settled down upon his spirit. Thirty yards of board fence nine feet high. Life to him seemed hollow, and existence but a burden.

Sighing, he dipped his brush and passed it along the topmost plank; repeated the operation; did it again; compared the insignificant whitewashed streak with the far-reaching continent of unwhitewashed fence, and sat down on a tree-box, discouraged. . . .

He began to think of the fun he had planned for this day, and his sorrows multiplied. Soon the free boys would come tripping along on all sorts of delicious expeditions, and they would make a world of fun of him for having to work—the very thought of it burnt him like fire. He got out his worldly wealth and examined it—bits of toys, marbles and trash; enough to buy an exchange of work maybe, but not half enough to buy so much as half an hour of pure freedom. So he returned his straited means to his pocket and gave up the idea of trying to buy the boys.

At this dark and hopeless moment an inspiration burst upon him! Nothing less than a great, magnificent inspiration.

He took up his brush and went tranquilly to work. Ben Rogers hove in sight presently—the very boy, of all boys, whose ridicule he had been dreading. Ben's gait was the hop-skip-and-jump—proof enough that his heart was light and his anticipations high. He was eating an apple, and giving a long, melodious whoop, at intervals, followed by a deep-toned ding-dong-dong, ding-dong-dong, for he was personating a steamboat.

As he drew near, he slackened speed, took the middle of the street, leaned far over to starboard and rounded to ponderously and with laborious pomp and circumstance —for he was personating the *Big Missouri,* and considered himself to be drawing nine feet of water. He was boat and captain and engine bells combined, so he had to imagine himself standing on his own hurricane deck giving the orders and executing them:

"Stop her, sir! Ting-a-ling-ling!" The headway ran almost out and he drew up slowly toward the sidewalk.

"Set her back on the stabbord! Ting-a-ling-ling! Chow! Ch-chow-wow, chow!" His right hand, meantime, describing stately circles—for it was representing a 40-foot wheel. . . .

Tom went on whitewashing—paid no attention to the steamboat. Ben stared a moment and then said:

"Hi-yi! You're up a stump, ain't you!"

No answer. Tom surveyed his last touch with the eye of an artist, then he gave his brush another gentle sweep and surveyed the result, as before. Ben ranged up along side of him. Tom's mouth watered for the apple, but he stuck to his work. Ben said:

"Hello, old chap, you got work to do, hey?"

Tom wheeled suddenly and said:

"Why, it's you Ben! I warn't noticing."

"Say, *I'm* going in a-swimming, *I* am. Don't you wish you could? But of course you'd druther work, wouldn't you? Course you would!"

Tom contemplated the boy a bit and said:

"What do you call work?"

"Why, ain't that work?"

Tom resumed his whitewashing and answered carelessly:

"Well, maybe it is, and maybe it ain't. All I know is, it suits Tom Sawyer."

"Oh, come, now, you don't mean to let on that you like it?"

The brush continued to move.

"Like it? Well, I don't see why I oughtn't to like it. Does a boy get a chance to whitewash a fence every day?"

That put the thing in a new light. Ben stopped nibbling his apple. Tom swept his brush daintily back and forth, stepped back to note the effect, added a touch here and there, criticized the effect again—Ben watching every move and getting more and more interested, more and more absorbed. Presently he said:

"Say, Tom, let me whitewash a little."

Tom considered, was about to consent; but he altered his mind:

"No—no—I reckon it wouldn't hardly do, Ben. You see, Aunt Polly's awful particular about this fence—right here on the street, you know—but if it was the back fence I wouldn't mind and she wouldn't. Yes, she's awful particular about this fence; it's got to be done very careful. I reckon there ain't one boy in a thousand, maybe two thousand, that can do it the way it's got to be done."

"No—is that so? Oh, come, now—lemme just try. Only just a little—I'd let you, if you was me, Tom."

"Ben, I'd like to, honest Injun; but Aunt Polly—now don't you see how I'm fixed? If you was to tackle this fence and anything was to happen to it—"

"Oh, shucks, I'll be just as careful. Now lemme try. Say, I'll give you the core of my apple."

"Well here—no, Ben, now don't. I'm afeared—"

"I'll give you all of it!"

Tom gave up the brush with reluctance in his face, but alacrity in his heart. And while the late steamer *Big Missouri* worked and sweated in the sun, the retired artist sat on a barrel in the shade close by, dangled his legs, munched his apple, and planned the slaughter of more innocents. There was no lack of material; boys happened along every little while. They came to jeer, but remained to whitewash. By the time Ben was fagged out, Tom had traded the next chance to Billy Fisher for a kite, in good repair, and when he played out, Johnny Miller bought in for a dead rat and a string to swing it with—and so on, hour after hour.

And when the middle of the afternoon came, from being a poor poverty-stricken boy in the morning, Tom was literally rolling in wealth. He had besides the things before mentioned, 12 marbles, part of a jew's harp, a piece of blue bottle glass to look through, a spool cannon, a key that wouldn't unlock anything, a fragment of chalk, a glass stopper of a decanter, a tin soldier, a couple of tadpoles, six firecrackers, a kitten with only one eye, a brass doorknob, a dog collar, the handle of a knife, four pieces of orange peel, and a dilapidated old window sash.

He had had a nice, good, idle time all the while—plenty of company—and the fence had three coats of whitewash on it! If he hadn't run out of whitewash, he would have bankrupted every boy in the village.

Tom said to himself that it was not such a hollow world after all. He had discovered a great law of human action without knowing it—namely, that in order to make a man or boy covet a thing, it is only necessary to make the thing difficult to attain. If he had been a great and wise philosopher, like the writer of this book, he would now have comprehended that work consists of whatever a body is obliged to do and that play consists of whatever a body is not obliged to do. The boy mused a while over the substantial change which had taken place in his worldly circumstances, and then wended toward headquarters to report.

Appendix F
Bibliography

For a more complete summary of books and articles pertinent to creative problem solving, the reader is referred to: *Bibliography on Creativity, Industrial Re-Search Institute, New York.* Additional bibliographies are included in some of the following sources:

Anderson, Harold H., (ed.). *Creativity and Its Cultivation.* New York: Harper & Bros., 1959.

Bloom, Benjamin S., and Broder, Louis J. *Problem Solving Processes of College Students.* Chicago: University of Chicago Press, 1950.

Bross, Irwin. *Design for Decision.* New York: Macmillan Co., 1953.

Company Climate and Creativity. New York: Industrial Relations News, 1959.

Crawford, Robert P. *The Techniques of Creative Thinking.* New York: Hawthorn Books, 1954.

"Creative Engineering." New York: American Society of Mechanical Engineers monograph, *circa* 1950.

Creativity and Conformity. Ann Arbor, Mich.: Foundation for Research on Human Behavior, 1958.

Cros, Pierre, *et al. Imagination–Undeveloped Resource.* Cambridge: Creative Thinking Associates, 1955.

Dewey, John. *How We Think.* Boston and New York: D. C. Heath and Co., 1933.

Duncker, Karl. "On Problem Solving." *Psychological Monographs,* Vol. 58, No. 5, 1945.

Fry, Thornton C. *Probability and Its Engineering Uses.* New York: Van Nostrand Co., Inc., 1928.

Ghiselin, Brewster, (ed.). *The Creative Process.* Berkeley: University of California Press, 1952.

Hadamard, Jacques. *The Psychology of Invention.* Princeton: Princeton University Press, 1945.
Hayakawa, Samuel I. *Language in Thought and Action.* New York: Harcourt, Brace, 1949.
Hix, C. F., and Alley, R. P. *Physical Laws and Effects.* New York: Wiley & Sons, 1958.
Hodnett, Edward. *The Art of Problem Solving.* New York: Harper & Bros., 1955.
Jevens, William S. *The Principles of Science.* London and New York: Macmillan Co., 1877.
Kogan, Zuce. *Essentials of Problem Solving.* New York: Arco Publishing Co., 1956.
Langer, Susanne K. *An Introduction to Symbolic Logic.* New York: Dover Publications, 1953.
Mill, John Stuart. *System of Logic.* London: Longmans, Green, Reader, and Dyer, 1868.
The Nature of Creative Thinking, a monograph. New York: Industrial Research Institute, 1952.
Osborn, Alex F. *Applied Imagination.* New York: Scribner, 1953.
Pearson, Donald. *Creativeness for Engineers.* Ann Arbor, Mich.: Edwards Brothers, Inc., 1958.
Pearson, Karl. *The Grammar of Science.* London: J. M. Dent and Sons, Ltd., 1937.
Polya, Gyorgy. *How To Solve It.* Garden City, N. Y.: Doubleday, 1957.
Raudsepp, E. "The Creative Engineer." *Machine Design,* 31: 22-26 May 28; 28-32 June 11; 27-30 June 25, 1959.
Research Conference on the Identification of Creative Scientific Talent. University of Utah Press, 1955, 1957, 1959.
Scientific American. New York: September 1958, Vol. 199, entire issue No. 3.
Simon, Leslie E. *Engineer's Manual of Statistical Methods.* New York: Wiley & Sons, 1941.
Ver Planck, D. W., and Teare, B. R. Jr. *Engineering Analysis.* New York: Wiley & Sons, 1954.
Von Fange, Eugene K. *Professional Creativity.* Englewood Cliffs, N. J.: Prentice-Hall, 1959.
Wallas, Graham. *The Art of Thought.* New York: Harcourt, Brace, 1926.
Wertheimer, Max. *Productive Thinking.* New York and London: Harper & Bros., 1945.
Whiting, Charles S. *Creative Thinking.* New York: Reinhold, 1958.
Wiener, Norbert. *The Human Use of Human Beings.* Boston: Houghton Mifflin, 1950.
Williams, John Davis. *The Compleat Strategyst.* New York: McGraw-Hill, 1954.
Wilson, Edgar Bright. *An Introduction to Scientific Research.* New York: McGraw-Hill, 1952.
Wolf, Abraham. *Essentials of Scientific Method.* New York: Macmillan, 1925.
Youtz, R. P. *Psychological Background of Applied Imagination.* Buffalo, N. Y.: Creative Education Foundation.

Index

Printed in U.S.A.